Alex Mabon was born in the Highlands of Scotland in 1939. On completion of schooling in Inverness he had a brief spell in journalism before enlisting in the Royal Air Force where he served ten years, during which time he travelled extensively in the Middle East and Far East.

On leaving the R.A.F. he was employed in various positions. This culminated in twenty years in property and business continuity management in the financial services industry in the City of London.

He is now retired and lives in Kent.

THE LADS FROM
THE FERRY

Alex Mabon

The Lads From The Ferry

Vanguard Press

A CIP catalogue record for this title is
available from the British Library
ISBN 1 84386 129 1

*Vanguard Press is an imprint of
Pegasus Elliot MacKenzie Publishers Ltd.
www.pegasuspublishers.com*

First Published in 2004

**Vanguard Press
Sheraton House Castle Park
Cambridge England**

Printed & Bound in Great Britain

This book is a work of fiction although some of the locations are real. It has been written in response to the never ending questions from a grandson to a grandfather about what life was like in "the old days."

The story is set in the 1940's 1950's and 1960's at a time when the world was a much more innocent place. If, on reading this, one twinge of memory is evoked, a smile is raised, or a tear is shed, then the effort will have been all worthwhile.

This is the story of John Urquhart and some of the other kids from the Ferry.

THIS BOOK IS
DEDICATED TO THE MEMORY Of

My Parents

and

My brother Don and my sister Cathie.

This book could not have been produced without the assistance of my wife Denise who contributed, cajoled, corrected and put up with my tantrums when things were not quite coming together.

A big thank you also to my daughter Karen for being so supportive, and to my grandsons, James Alexander Weighell and Jonathan Charles Weighell just for being my grandsons.

Rushing waters, rumbling, tumbling,
Flowing down from mountain streams,
Weave through islets, draped in beauty,
Islands of my childhood dreams.

PROLOGUE

APRIL 2003

The old man settled himself comfortably into his seat as the mid-day train from Kings Cross to Inverness pulled out of the London station.

It had been a long time since his last visit to Inverness. Nearly forty years. He wondered just how much the town had changed.

He opened his suitcase and extracted the urn that he had been given. He knew what he was expected to do. It was simple enough. Scatter the contents of the urn in the Ness Islands.

Chapter One

INVERNESS, SCOTLAND
CHRISTMAS DAY 1938

The midwife dismounted her bicycle outside the home of the expectant mother and chained the bike to the front gate, which was hanging on one hinge. She looked around, half expecting something, or somebody, to emerge from behind the fence. It was her first visit to the area. For six months she had carefully manipulated all her call-outs to ensure she avoided this particular part of town. The unexpected absence of one of her colleagues, on sick leave as the result of a nervous breakdown, had resulted in a late change of roster. It was bad enough to have to work on Christmas Day, but to have to visit this particular area made her nervous.

With a sigh of relief she realised that the street was empty. She picked up her bag and proceeded into the house.

An hour later the midwife exited the house having executed her duty, as she saw it, of bringing 'another screaming brat into the world'. She hated children with a passion, and was seriously considering reverting to her former role of prison warder, in the maximum security wing of the local prison. She reflected on the child she had just delivered. "They get uglier and noisier every day, but this one really drew the short straw," she muttered to herself.

She was so intent on this thought that, on mounting her bicycle, she failed to notice the young lads disappearing around the corner.

She made two more calls that day, bringing life into the world. Early that evening she arrived at the home she shared with her daughter and three month old granddaughter in the posh Hill district of the town. She reflected, over a few glasses of sweet sherry, on just how peaceful her life was. Perhaps, she thought, she would give the midwifery practice a few more months before making any decision on change.

In the very early hours of the following morning she was called out to an emergency birth in the Crown district of the town. She was stopped by the police five minutes later. They pointed out that she was riding her bicycle without lights. She was at a loss to understand this. She had checked them the previous morning, prior to her run to the Ferry district.

She was arrested for riding a bicycle without lights whilst under the influence of drink. Arriving home, by black maria, at ten o'clock that morning, she was met by a neighbourhood preparing for church. The neighbours were aghast. Most of them had never seen a black maria before.

After a brief spell of treatment at the local mental hospital, she applied for her old job at the prison. She was turned down on the grounds that she had a criminal record.

She vowed never to return to The Ferry District.

Chapter Two

John Urquhart arrived in the world on a cold snowy Christmas Day in 1938. Unlike a more famous child, born on the same day nearly two thousand years before, there was nothing spectacular about his birth. No guiding star, no wise men, no kings bearing gifts. This was the Ferry district, and the most one could hope for in the miracle stakes was to have a roof over one's head, a crust of bread on the table, and a pair of shoes that did not leak.

It was an idyllic time. It was a time when rowing boats trailing fishing nets operated on the River Ness. There was one church to every one thousand residents, and crime was restricted to the odd town centre drunk on a Saturday night. Dark clouds were hovering over Europe in anticipation of a long war, but there was peace in the air in Inverness.

John's family home was no manger. It was a council-owned ground floor maisonette comprising of a living room, kitchen, bathroom and two bedrooms. There was a small front garden bordered by a wooden paling fence. The fence was broken and the gate hung on one hinge, but this was normal for the area. The house was one in a block of four.

His arrival into the world was greeted by the ugliest woman he was ever likely to meet, (who fortunately turned out to be the midwife), his mother, his father and four siblings comprising three sisters and a brother.

When he was a few months old his family were all

provided with gasmasks in anticipation of an air raid on the town. An air raid would probably have improved the ambience of the Ferry, but it did not materialise. John's gas mask was as big as a carrycot, and had a window on top, in order that a regular check could be made that he was still breathing.

With seven in the family the allocation of bed space was complicated. The sleeping space was eased by his mother and father having a fold up bed in the living room, whilst John shared a room with his elder brother and one sister.

The Highland winters were bitter. There was no heating in the bedrooms and Jack Frost was a nightly visitor, leaving behind his calling card of ice-encrusted windows, in patterns worthy of the talents of Picasso. Covering the windows with newspaper had little effect in keeping out the cold.

It was standard practice for a house brick to be heated in the fire or oven and then be used as a means of heating the bed. For those who could afford it a stone hot water bottle was a better alternative. Beds were covered in all manner of clothing in order to keep out the cold.

The coal fire in the living room was banked up every night with coke, clinkers, or coal dust in an attempt to keep the room warm during the night. It was a constant battle to keep the room clean as coal dust settled everywhere. The visit of the chimney sweep resulted in the need to cover what furniture there was. There were no carpets, the floor was either bare, or covered in linoleum. Failure to sweep the chimney on a regular basis often resulted in a chimney fire. The sound of fire engines would bring everybody out in the street. Only to be disappointed on hearing "it was just a chimney fire."

The fire brigade came to the conclusion that a number

of local residents deliberately avoided paying for a chimney sweep as the Fire Brigade Service was free. A risky business. But times were very hard.

Within a few years of John's arrival in the world three further brothers arrived to bring the family number to ten. John noticed that the midwife attending the birth of one of his brothers appeared to be nervous, and had a constant twitch in her eye. She had a bicycle dynamo and light strapped to her waist.

The sign of nerves became apparent when the midwife dropped the new born baby. As luck would have it the baby landed on his head. Landing on one of the limbs could have had long-term work implications. The kids from the Ferry were not expected to achieve greatness. Just survive.

With the birth of John's younger brother a further part was acquired from the midwife's bicycle This meant that John's next door neighbour had obtained sufficient parts to be the proud owner of a prototype Raleigh FS (Ferry Special) bicycle. The bicycle wheels did not match, and the attachment of two dynamos, two bells, and a multi-coloured frame looked odd. But this did not detract from the pride of ownership.

The new arrivals made the division of bed space an even bigger challenge. The family now had two bedrooms and a living room, into which ten bodies had to be accommodated. To say they were a close family would be stating the obvious. Mattresses on the floor overcame the shortage of beds.

Bathing for the younger children in John's family was conducted on a Sunday night, in a metal tub in front of an open coal fire, usually with carbolic soap. The children did not smell very nice when they were finished bathing, but they were clean. Bathing in front of an open fire was not without its dangers, as a fusillade of sparks would frequently erupt from the fire onto a naked body. The moment the children stepped out of the hot bath they were in danger of freezing to death, as the rest of the house was icy cold. Bath time was always conducted to the sound of Radio Luxembourg and 'we are the Ovaltinies happy girls and boys'. Being a member of a radio club, bringing with it a badge and newsletter, was a necessary part of early childhood.

Despite the superior attitude adopted by some of the town residents towards the Ferry in the 1940s, the Ferry estate was a much sought after place to live. This was not due to the ambience of the district. It was because there was no alternative housing. The shortage of housing resulted in several families squatting in ex-military huts on the edge of the town. Tinkers formed a large part of the community, decanting themselves onto any available field.

But the Ferry folk, the squatters, and the tinkers were by no means the most deprived people in the town. The Poor House existed. It was no figment of the imagination. The world of Charles Dickens was still hanging on in Inverness.

Chapter Three

A tall military figure stood in the doorway of John's house. John looked up at the dark skinned man and wondered who he was. The well-tanned soldier was dressed in army khaki. The soldier spoke. "Hello lad" he said, "I'm your Dad."

John looked past his newfound Dad, and saw a soldier, in the same uniform as his Dad, standing outside the front door of Sandy Roberts' house. The side door of Sandy's house opened as the soldier was rapping on the front door. John saw the figure of Sandy's 'uncle', Jocky Winngate, a regular visitor to the house, come out the side door, holding his shirt in one hand. He was barefoot. His other hand was holding up his trousers.

"There's a soldier at your front door, Mr Winngate." John called out. "You'll miss him if you go out the back door."

Sandy Roberts' father turned round at the sound of John's voice. He peered around the corner of his house. Just in time to see Jocky Winngate disappear over the back fence.

Following the end of the war in Europe in May 1945, street parties were held. Tables, chairs, flags, and bunting made from white bed sheets, dyed red and blue, were acquired. The Ferry residents all sat down to an unimaginable feast of ice cream, jelly, homemade cakes, and lemonade.

A giant bonfire was lit with items involuntarily

contributed by the local council. Fences and wooden garden sheds were fair game.

Dancing was held in the streets well into the early hours. In the absence of the men-folk, women danced with women. There was hardly a dry eye, as some of them realised that their loved ones would soon be home from the war. For others, those who had received the dreaded telegram, there was the realisation that their loved ones would not return. It was a time of joy, and a time of sadness.

Life quickly resumed its pre-war routine for his father and elder brother and John began to take an interest in their leisure activities. Listening to the Scotland England football matches, huddled round the Bush valve radio, was a particularly exciting time. The Press described these matches as 'a clash with the auld enemy'. His father used to get quite worked up during the course of the game, frequently muttering 'bloody English' under his breath.

John was eight years old before he realised that England and Scotland had fought on the same side during the war.

John's father was fortunate in that, on his return from the war, he resumed his pre-war occupation. This often entailed working seven days a week. But with so many mouths to feed, there was little option. There was no assistance from social security or child benefits in those days.

Chapter Four

Whilst the Ferry was no better, or no worse, than any other housing estate in Britain at the time, it was, nevertheless, an area where the working class lived. This is a bit misleading as most of the people living in the Ferry were still aspiring to be working class. There was no lack of desire to work, but jobs were few and far between.

There were clear demarcation lines between the Ferry and those who lived in the posh parts of town. In simplistic terms this meant anywhere other than the Ferry. An aspiration to move out of one's class was for the dreamer. The Ferry folk knew their place in life.

The Ferry area comprised six streets, namely North Drive, South Drive, West Drive, Kessock Avenue, Kessock Road and Craigton Avenue. Navigating the streets for a total stranger was particularly difficult. South Drive was located at the bottom of the estate, in the normally accepted southern position. North Drive was in the West position, whilst West Drive was on the East side of the estate. This created no difficulties for the residents, as most of them had no idea whether they were coming or going at the best of times.

In 1945 the Beauly Firth overflowed and Kessock Road, the main road to the Ferry, was flooded for two days. The more cynical of the residents held the view that the flood waters took one look at the Ferry and decided to retreat.

The estate was one of the safest places a child could be raised in the early 1940s. Houses had an open door policy and neighbours, in hair curlers and slippers, conducted gossip over the garden fence without fear of violation. Personal possessions were sacrosanct. Council property was another matter, and visits by the police to the estate were a regular occurrence.

Apart from the inevitable Saturday night contretemps between husbands and wives, or warring neighbours (usually prompted by a touch of the water of life), and the almost daily search by the police for missing council equipment, life was fairly mundane for John.

He was a young child at the time. It was possible therefore that murder, rape, or even gang warfare occurred after his normal bedtime of seven o'clock in the evening. Except on Sunday, when his bedtime was dictated by where he was on the tin bath rota, and the speed with which the water could be heated on an open fire.

Anderson air raid shelters had been installed in the rear gardens of houses in the ratio of one shelter to every four houses. The shelters provided a great source of play for the children, despite the constant smell trapped within the metal walls, and the regular flooding. The shelters soon became known as The Sock Factories. This name was arrived at through childish innocence, brought about by the curiosity of Jean Morgan, who, whilst playing hide and seek, decided to hide in the shelter.

Jean, aged four at the time, rushed out of the shelter, within seconds of entry, screaming at the top of her voice "They're having sex! They're having sex!" The girls in the Ferry were very precocious.

Her screams prompted John, and Sandy, to rush into the shelter, not quite sure what to expect.

The last thing they expected to see was Chrissie

Forbes and Harry MacKenzie (two of the neighbours) in a state of nudity, and in a compromising position. Sandy rushed out of the shelter shouting "He's killing her, he's killing her", whilst John rushed out screaming "They're making socks, they're making socks." John had never heard the word 'sex' before.

This news brought a crowd of spectators to the shelter, including Mrs Forbes's husband. The crowd were in favour of there being a sock factory because of the shortage of clothing and the need for clothing coupons. They could not have cared less who was getting murdered. Apart from Mr Forbes, who had fairly definite views on who was going to be laid to rest.

A large field lay behind the houses in the Ferry and this enabled John and his friends to re-enact war games and cowboys and indians. Reality was added to the activities by the regular finding of ammunition, including bullets and a live grenade, which had been previously stored in an adjacent warehouse. Playing with live ammunition was not without consequence however. It was swiftly brought to an end following injury to seven children when the grenade exploded. Aircraft recognition cards and booklets were treasured finds, and the children spent many a happy hour trying to collect a set of cards of German fighters and bombers.

It was whilst playing in the Ferry field that John had his first experience of physical assault. The council had provided swings as part of a play area for the younger children. A dispute arose over the use of the swings. In traditional Ferry fashion the matter was resolved by one of the older girls lobbing a brick into the fracas.

John's head and the brick collided. There was blood everywhere. John's sister fainted, and the remaining children ran away. He required seven stitches. He was just grateful that the assailant had not found the grenade.

A month after the brick incident John experienced another assault when a bag of lime was tipped from the back of a lorry onto his head. John was playing hide and seek at the time. This was the chosen way of telling him that he had been found. Once again the assailant was a girl. A blow to the head, whether caused by a midwife or a rampant female, was the most common form of assault to any child in the Ferry. John was beginning to get a complex about women. He was beginning to feel that they did not like him. At the age of five he was already paranoid.

Scavenging was a means of play, and frequently a few of the braver children would venture to the local municipal rubbish tip, to see what could be salvaged. In the eyes of the children the rubbish tip seemed to be as high as a mountain. Often a child would tumble from the top to the bottom, oblivious to the rubbish in the way. Screaming seagulls dive-bombing, and the odd rat running within inches of an outstretched hand, were acceptable challenges for the prize of a battered, but still serviceable, metal cast Matchbox car, dumped from one of the rich houses.

The scavenging on the rubbish tip came to an abrupt end, however, when a major find was made.

John will never forget the look on Sandy's face when John uncovered, and proudly held up, what appeared to be a human arm and leg. The police were called. It transpired that the body parts were from a child-size tailor's dummy. Sandy was of a particularly nervous disposition and had to be sedated. John took home the dummy arm and leg. "They may," he reflected, "just come in useful one day."

Encouraged, by all the parents, was the collection of loose coal from a local coal yard, and from the railway line which ran alongside the playing field. There always seemed to be an abundance of coal beside the tracks. The stokers on the Inverness to Dingwall steam trains were very sympathetic to the needs of the Ferry folk.

Fuel for the open fire was anything that could burn and was of no further value. There was something exotic in the taste of hot buttered toast, made in front of an open fire, when the main fuel was old footwear.

From the mid 1940s a fish and chip van (the 'chippie') served the Ferry area. This provided a regular feast on Fridays for those fortunate enough to have a weekly wage packet which allowed them to afford this luxury. A drunken husband, staggering home, bereft of his wages, having donated generously in several of the many watering holes between his place of employment and his front door, would clutch a fish and chip supper in his arms as a peace offering. This was the Ferry at its best, as neighbours listened to the sounds when irate wives lay into errant husbands, to the chorus of raucous seagulls.

At a time when there were *'Bluebirds over the White Cliffs of Dover'* and *'Nightingales sang in Berkeley Square',* the Ferry had to be content with down-market seagulls.

By the time he was seven John's view on the safety and friendliness of the Ferry began to alter. The estate was still friendly during the day, with neighbour helping neighbour. But at night time the atmosphere darkened. This change over a short period of time was brought about by the men folk having returned from the war, the availability of alcohol, and, in many cases, a feeling of despair at the lack of employment.

The Ferry did not have the monopoly on drunkenness however, this was a problem shared with most of the town. Drunks lying in the doorways of the town centre shops shortly after the public houses closed at nine o'clock in the evening were a normal feature. The Black Maria police vans were a regular sight on the streets on a Saturday night, as they ferried inebriates from the hostelry to the police station and then home after a night in the cells.

Regular visits were made to the local scrap merchants, where additional housekeeping money could be obtained by disposing of old clothing, bottles, or scrap metal. A cry of 'any old rags and bones' would bring householders out to the visiting horse-drawn cart of the rag-and-bone-man. The reward for the discarded items would be a goldfish or a few pence.

Screams of "Ma I want a goldfish" would echo along the street, followed by the sound of a thump and wailing, as a mother explained to her child that he was wearing the only rags they had. Screaming, at the top of her voice "You can wear a torn pair of trousers to school but you can't wear a goldfish."

It was a struggle to survive, and was best summed up by one of John's friends (aged eight, going on eighty) who stated, "We may be scum, but we're good scum." His friend was clearly destined to be a psychiatrist one day, or a patient.

In the late forties the resourcefulness of those living in the Ferry reached new heights. New houses were being added to the Hilton council estate in the town. One of the features of the new houses was a rotary clothes line in each garden. Overnight the rotary lines disappeared. The following day similar rotary lines appeared in some back gardens in the Ferry. Needless to say the Highland Constabulary, the scourge of the Ferry, were mystified at the loss.

The Ferry people lived with dignity, regardless of the difficulties thrown on them by outside forces. There was a necessary closeness between the snobbery of the Hill residents and the working class of the Ferry. The Hill businessmen needed the Ferry folk in order to prosper. The Ferry folk needed the Hill folk in order to survive.

Greed and hunger made for strange bedfellows.

John's father frequently warned him. "Don't trust the sods. Avoid the Hill district if you can. If you do have to go up there, make sure you have a reliable witness. The police have the whole place under surveillance."

The gullibility of the younger children was exploited by their elder siblings on every possible occasion.

On one such occasion, at the age of four, John and all his friends were singing the nursery rhyme 'Old MacDonald had a Farm'. Hearing them chant this, John's older brother, James, took it into his head to advise the children that 'Old MacDonald' lived just around the corner in Craigton Avenue. "The best time to see him and his animals is early on Sunday morning," he added helpfully.

And so it was that on the following Sunday, John and his mates all trooped round to see MacDonald's farm. John looked at the doors and eventually found a door with a metal nameplate reading W MacDonald. It did not strike the children as odd that the door was attached to a first floor maisonette.

The residents of Craigton Avenue thought Armageddon had arrived when, at a few minutes past seven on a Sunday morning, they heard the repeated incantation "We want to see your animals, we want to see your animals." This was followed by a rendition of "Old MacDonald had a Farm."

Willie MacDonald woke up, thinking he had gone mad. He could hear angel voices singing about animals. He realised, eventually, after the fourth rendition, that the noise was directed at him, and was not a call from Heaven, but was, in fact, outside his front door. Nursing a blinding hangover, brought about by his normal Saturday night of pints of Heavy followed by Whisky chasers, he descended the stairs and opened his front door.

As understanding dawned on Willie, he flew off the handle. Dropping his pyjama trousers he shouted, "I'll show you my bloody animals, you little sods. I'll tell all your fathers, although you're probably all Jocky Winngate's brats."

The boys, led by Sidney Brown, a sickly looking child, fled.

Irene Norman aged four, and Susan Simpson, aged three, stood there, nonplussed, looking at the naked MacDonald.

"I can see why you're called Wee Willie MacDonald," stated Irene, "no wonder your wife left you." Saying this she pulled Susan down the road. Susan was in turn dragging her young cousin, who was on a holiday visit.

Irene had other things to do. She had just remembered that it was Animal Torment Day. The event was held annually, and Robert Johnson had beaten her the previous year. He had managed to tie the tails of a cat and dog together, with a firecracker forming part of the tying process. Mary had been beaten not so much by a short head, as by a short tail.

This therefore was the background in which John and the rest of the kids from the Ferry grew up. It gave them the lust to better themselves, to achieve greatness, to go forth into the world.

But Jocky Winngate did not go forth. Jocky stayed in Inverness and multiplied.

Chapter Five

By the time John was aged four his elder brother James had filled his head with wonderful stories. John believed everything his big brother told him, particularly stories about life at school.

John knew exactly what to expect when he turned up for school for the first time. He stood outside the school, trying to break away from his sister who was holding him in an iron grip.

But John had an imagination well beyond his years. He did not require an older head to fantasise for him. In his mind he could see exactly what was happening behind the grim walls. This is what John saw.

Mr Jefferson, the deputy head teacher at the Kessock Primary School, looked out of the window overlooking the main entrance to the school. He surveyed the influx of new pupils being escorted to school by their elder siblings or parents. He mused on what he was doing in this part of the world, but then remembered the slight mishap at the all-boys school in Paisley.

He lovingly touched the new leather strap he held in his hands, purchased direct from a discreet mail order store in Leeds. "Come on, my little ones, "he muttered, his eyes glazing over as he gazed down at the group of lads with the small tight buttocks, being dragged, weeping, through the school gates. "I'll show you what crying is all about."

At the same time as Mr Jefferson, better known as Slimey, was eyeing the new arrivals, Mr Scott, the headmaster of the school, was briefing the staff in the padded room used for staff recreation and training. Twelve teachers were present, four of them new to the school. They were the replacements for the four teachers who, by some strange coincidence, had all decided to emigrate to Australia at the end of the previous term.

Demonstrations by external consultants were taking place in different parts of the padded room. In one corner a sergeant from the Commando Training School at Spean Bridge was advising the teachers on aspects of self-defence, specialising on how to beat children without leaving a mark.

A second corner was occupied by a constable from the Highland Constabulary. He was pointing to a montage of pictures of small children all aged about five years old. "This", he began, "is Tommy Brown. The picture was taken by an undercover officer posing as a dustman. It shows Tommy in the process of stalking a cat with a machete."

The officer then pointed to the picture of a young girl. "And this" he continued, "is Marie Winngate. She will nick anything. She is our chief suspect in the theft of fifty gas masks from the underground bunker at the Town Hall."

The headmaster looked at the photographs. The thought of a pupil using a machete could have an effect on the new teachers. He looked at his new staff. With a sigh of relief he realised that none of them knew what a machete was. 'Thank God', he thought, 'the Education Authority has not sent any brainy ones'.

In another corner of the room, a salesman from the Gorbals Leather Company (Specialists In All Kinds Of Leather Gear, Discreet Enquiries Welcome), was demonstrating a new type of leather strap on a tailor's dummy of a small child. The salesman punched his hand in the air. "Excellent" he excitedly cried, "this will teach the little sods." This was the second dummy he had used at the school. The first one had been put out for rubbish after the salesman had removed an arm and two legs in an over-enthusiastic demonstration.

Meanwhile, in the remaining corner of the room, a teacher was throwing himself against the padded wall, exclaiming as he did so "I will be strong. I will be strong."

At the entrance to the staff room stood a priest. He was giving individual tuition to the new teachers on the best way to hold a three-foot cross on entering a classroom.

But John knew all this before he stepped through the school doors. He knew this was what school was like. His brother James had told him, and if James had said it, it must be true.

The star of the six primary schools serving Inverness in the 1940s was the Kessock Primary School. Feared by the other schools – the 'Kessie', as it was affectionately known by the townsfolk, but known as 'Jocky Winngate's Orphanage' by the more knowledgeable Ferry folk – was an early training ground for those doomed to a life of poverty and obscurity.

With the exception of those who became criminal masterminds, or were locked up certified as insane.

John and Sandy went to the 'Kessie'.

At the age of five they were doomed for the rest of their lives. There was no hope for them.

John's two most abiding memories of the 'Kessie'

School were to be the school dinners and the daily use of 'the belt', as the leather strap used by one or two of the more sadistic teachers was called. On balance John thought that 'the belt' punishment was less damaging to the health than the dollops of tapioca and jam served for school dinners. Meals arrived at the school in huge metal containers – the smell of the food contaminated the whole school.

He frequently missed school dinners and walked the half-mile each lunchtime to his grandmother's home for a snack of bread and margarine with sugar topping. His grandmother and grandfather lived in a small terraced cottage. Conditions there were more basic than in John's Ferry home. There was no inside toilet or electricity. The lighting came from fixed gas mantle lamps, and paraffin lamps strategically placed about the house. The only heat in the house was from the open fire, which also served as the cooking range. A solid metal soot encrusted kettle was permanently placed by the fire. John lost count of the number of uncles and aunts who also lived there. He was beginning to realise that the family Ferry home was quite palatial.

School dinners were supplemented by a free issue of milk. The children competed fiercely for the position of milk monitor, as it allowed them to escape from the classroom for a few moments, thereby reducing the prospect of receiving a 'belting' for a misdemeanour of which they were totally innocent.

At home a daily dose of cod liver oil and orange juice concentrate was forced down the throats of the children, to provide essential vitamins and prevent scurvy.

School was over a mile from John's home. This walk was taken every day, regardless of weather conditions. In the winter there was often deep snow. John always knew snow was expected when he saw his father putting cardboard, or linoleum, in the children's shoes.

John's route to school was terrifying. He had to walk past the harbour, an area full of foreign seamen, and a public house known as The Harbour Inn. This place always frightened him.

He imagined it at night time full of drunken sailors and pirates. In his mind he saw all the pirates, each with only one leg, an eye patch, and a parrot on his shoulder. A blood-encrusted cutlass would hang from the pirate's belt, ready for use on the first child caught glancing in the window.

John knew that female vampires lived in the Harbour Inn because the children had heard the grown-ups talk about them. The grown-ups always referred to them as 'ladies of the night', but this did not fool the children. They had seen enough posters of vampires at the local cinema to know what women were called who worked at night.

On several occasions John saw the curtain on the inn window twitch. A face, with lips covered in blood, looked out, and a beckoning finger, also covered in blood, urged him to enter. He ran away, screaming, on each occasion.

Writing materials in the school for his first two years consisted of a slate and a piece of metal used to etch the slate. Each desk was equipped with an ink well in the hope that paper and ink supplies would one day arrive at the school.

Times tables were learned by rote, when all the pupils would chant out 'seven times seven is forty nine, seven times eight is fifty six'. Inevitably there was always one pupil out of tune who insisted that 'seven times seven is forty-three'. Without blinking an eyelid or turning her head, the teacher would bounce the blackboard duster off the child's head, from a distance of fifteen feet.

There was very little chance of any lasting harm, as

most of the children were brain dead before they even started school. This was only partly due to the carelessness of midwives, and the homicidal tendencies of young girls.

Danger sometimes arose at school due to the enthusiasm of the new pupils. Little hands would shoot up in the air as the children shouted "please miss, please miss," in an effort to attract the attention of the teacher when the children knew the answer to a question. The stampede to put the answer on the blackboard would frequently result in the younger children being trampled under-foot. John caught on to this practice quite quickly, and would often stick his hand in the air, pretending he knew the answer to the question, hoping that he would not be the child chosen to answer.

Playtime at school lasted fifteen minutes, during which time the children had to cram in as many activities as possible. For the boys, old newspapers tied with string, served as a football in the absence of the real thing. Marbles was another firm favourite. Steel ball-bearings stolen from British Rail or the bus depot, were prized possessions.

The major play activity of the girls was hopscotch, or running in a pack giggling, led by Susan Simpson, into the boys' toilets. It was a nerve wracking experience for the boys, some of whom never recovered.

End of playtime each day was announced by the ringing of a hand-bell. Pupils would go from class to class in crocodile lines. One of the pupils achieved God-like status when he removed the clapper from the bell during one lunch break, allowing the children to have an additional fifteen minutes play time. He also achieved the school record for the number of 'straps' received as punishment. John could swear that he saw Slimey Jefferson with tears in his eyes as he dealt out the punishment. John wondered if Slimey had a soft spot for children. John was puzzled. This was not the image his brother James had described.

The school had been built with stone in the nineteenth century. The screams of the children, and the smell of the school dinners, were contained within the walls.

Health inspections were a major feature of the school curriculum. It was not unusual to see one of the pupils with head covered in purple dye following a 'nits' inspection. It was as a result of a school eye examination that John had to wear spectacles. At the age of eight this came as a body blow. He reasoned that not only would this lessen his chances of getting in the school football team, but no girl would ever look at him!

One of the major events in the school calendar was sports day. This was usually marked by an argument between over-zealous mums, convinced that their child had been robbed of victory. This was the only sign of interest in their children shown by some of the parents from one year to the next.

In his second year at the 'Kessie' John was selected for both the wheelbarrow race and the sack race. He never got a chance to participate. Mid-way through the morning's sporting fiesta the headmaster took the decision to abandon the games. This was on police advice.

On the morning of the school sports Inspector Berk of the Highland Constabulary had briefed his constables on the task they were about to face.

"This is the big one" he began, "the Kessie Sports Day. I want you to check all your equipment. Make sure nothing is loose that can be used against you. And," he continued, "make sure the dogs are in pairs at all times. One of the little nutters is known to have used a machete."

The inspector looked at his troops. There were a few

pale faces. They had been advised by their experienced colleagues on what to expect.

"Right," said the Inspector, "last chance. Anybody wish to pull out?"

There was a shuffle of feet as each of the constables waited to see who had the courage to back out. Collectively they were thinking, "They're only kids. It can't be that bad."

"Off we go then, chaps" Inspector Berk said, delighted that his troops had held firm. "Don't forget to leave your next-of-kin details with Sergeant Brown before you leave the station."

The sports day began at ten o'clock. By five past ten there was bedlam. It was prompted by Tommy Ross's mother, who took umbrage at her son being disqualified in the three-legged race, despite winning by ten yards. It was pointed out to Mrs Ross that the term three-legged actually meant two children being tied together. The use of a leg from a tailor's dummy as substitute for a child did not meet the criteria.

Mrs Ross had no idea what criteria meant, but she knew her son had won the race, and he deserved the prize. In the meantime Jessie Williams and Betty Fraser, the runners-up, were sobbing their hearts out.

Mr Scott, the headmaster, chose the easy way out. He awarded a prize of three-pence to each of the three children, Tommy, Jessie and Betty. He explained to the mothers that this seemed a sensible compromise to the problem. This however was the 'Kessie' sports day. Common sense would not be allowed to get in the way of a good argument. The word 'compromise' totally threw Mrs Ross. She was still trying to get her head round 'criteria'.

Mrs Ross demanded a further three-pence on the

grounds that the other half of Tommy's partnership, i.e. the dummy leg, had received nothing.

Betty Fraser's mother replied to this request by dumping all the raw eggs, held for the egg and spoon race, onto Mrs Ross's head. This prompted those children who were down as competitors in the egg and spoon race to go hysterical, as they realised their race would not be held. All the parents joined in the fracas which followed. The leader of the gang against Mrs Fraser was the school Religious Education teacher, who had loaned the eggs to the school. She had them on trust from the grocer, who was holding her ration book as security.

Whilst the fracas was going on John slipped away, clutching the dummy leg discarded by Tommy Ross. John was now the owner of two dummy legs and one dummy arm.

At midnight, when he eventually got home, Inspector Berk reflected on the results of the day. One police dog bitten, one police dog missing, and two constables in hospital with head wounds as the result of being hit with a handbag containing a brick.

'All in all, a good day' he thought. 'A big improvement on last year, when the Army had to be called in'.

The 'Kessie' did not have a school uniform. It is fair to state however that all the children wore similar clothing, inasmuch that each child wore second-hand clothing, handed down from sibling to sibling. John drew the line at wearing his sister's frock. Serviceable clothing which could not be handed down through a family was donated for jumble sales. These were a great source of cheap clothing but more importantly as far as the children were concerned a source of books and toys.

It was quite common for John to find one of his

classmates wearing an item of clothing that John's parents had discarded, whilst John sat there with a pair of shoes previously owned by another of his classmates.

This practice of buying second-hand clothes had its pitfalls however!

On John's first day at school he was dragged to school by one of his sisters, who totally ignored his screams that he did not want to go there. He had two elder sisters at the 'Kessie' at the time. They had been allocated the responsibility of ensuring that he got to school. The word 'safely' was not mentioned, just "take him there."

At the end of the first day at school the teacher, by now despairing at the density of the new group of pupils, prepared for the children to go home. By this time a squad of cleaners had arrived to mop up the liquid on the floor. The concept of putting one's hand up stating "please miss, can I leave the room?" had not yet been grasped by all the pupils.

The teacher handed the children their coats. She looked at John.

"Which jacket is yours, boy?" she asked.

John pointed to his jacket.

The teacher picked it up, looked on the name tag inside and asked, "Is there anybody here to see you home, Billy?"

John replied in the affirmative, but wondered why his name had been changed.

Fifteen minutes later his sister had still not appeared. He was beginning to wonder if he had been abandoned. Another puddle began to form on the floor. The teacher looked at John and decided that the best course of action was to get a senior pupil to take him home.

She summoned one of the elder girls and asked the question "Do you know where Billy Wilson lives?"

The girl looked a bit gormless and replied "Yes,

miss." This was probably the only question she had answered all day.

"Right," said the teacher, pointing at John, "take him there."

On this command the imbecile grabbed John by the hand and pulled him out of the classroom.

Fifteen minutes later John and the School Moron were standing outside a house in West Drive. John lived in South Drive. The door was answered by yet another gormless looking girl. The Ferry was full of them.

"Here," said Miss Moron to Miss Gormless, "he's all yours." She pushed John into the house.

The resident gormless girl followed John into the house. John sat down and looked around. The room was better furnished than his old South Drive home.

"Who are you?" the girl asked.

"I'm Billy Wilson" he replied.

She rushed from the room screaming "Ma."

By this time John was quite desperate for the toilet and began to explore the house. He passed two bedrooms on the way with just one bed in each. Things were looking up. He had gone to school terrified, not knowing what to expect, and here he was with a new home. He had not realised that the school gave new pupils better names and homes.

He pondered briefly on whether he would miss his parents and brothers and sisters, but by the time he had finished thinking about it he had already forgotten them.

He returned to the living room. He had heard his parents talk about West Drive. It was the up-market part of the Ferry. He had no idea what this meant but it sounded promising. Here he was day one at school, with a new name and living up-market. He had already cracked it.

His dreams were shattered a few minutes later when a

large and ugly woman with red hair entered the room.

"Who are you?" she demanded.

"I'm Billy Wilson" he replied. He was not quite sure whether he should call her Mum or Miss.

"No, you're not" she retorted "this is Billy Wilson."

She dragged into the room a lad about five years older than John.

John opened his mouth to make his case when the lad screamed "Ma, he's got my old jacket on."

This was enough for John to wet himself.

John was thrown out of the house and escorted home to South Drive. He had been an hour late coming home from school. One sister had assumed that the other was picking him up. Nobody had noticed that he was missing. He vowed to run away from home as soon as he had saved enough money. With only one penny a week pocket money, he realised that it would probably take him a few weeks.

As an ongoing precaution, John examined all his new second-hand clothes to ensure that nametags were removed from any items bought at jumble sales. Any clothing received from overseas units of The Salvation Army and Red Cross was scrutinised even more closely.

The name Billy Wilson he could live with. But the thought of being called Mustapha was a bit too much.

He did not want to suffer from a Split Personality Disorder by the age of six.

In July each year the school end of term summer holidays started. The euphoria from the teaching staff was offset by the wave of depression which hit the Ferry as the parents realised that their children would be home for a few weeks.

It made no difference to some parents. They had not even realised that the children had been going to school.

Chapter Six

Jocky Winngate, the supervisor at Jock's Kitchen, and alleged father of most of the Ferry kids, adjusted his gas-mask and watched his staff as, half-blinded by their own gas-masks, they groped their way around the steaming vats of boiling food disguised as school dinners. Jocky was pleased with himself. The gas-masks were working. Absenteeism was down and there were fewer incidents of staff falling into the vats, overcome by the smell. Only the previous week there had been complaints from one of the schools when a pair of spectacles was found in the tapioca pudding.

He vowed to thank his daughter Marie once again, for her initiative in obtaining the gas-masks. She had shown a mark of genius in bluffing her way into the secure bunker of the Town Hall, by pretending she was looking for the Provost in order to discuss the poverty of the Ferry. Not one of the Town Hall officials had thought it odd that she only appeared to be about five years old, had no shoes, and could barely speak.

Marie had to leave town at the age of seven as a result of the Town Hall incident and the theft of the furniture from the headmaster's study at the 'Kessie'. She now lived with her Aunt Jessie in Glasgow. Jocky wondered what had happened to Marie's identical twin sister. Jocky had never married. The children were the result of a relationship between himself and a Government Health Inspector. She had called at Jock's Kitchen one day following complaints. She had never heard of Jocky's reputation with the women. It took her exactly ten minutes to find out. By which time she was pregnant.

Agreement was reached on the twin daughters. Jocky would keep one. The other child would go with the mother, the Health Inspector, who lived with her mother in the Hill District. Jocky had told Marie that her mother had died giving birth. The Health Inspector from up the Hill did not want her daughter to know that her father worked as a school meals supervisor, and that he was from the Ferry, so she had advised her daughter that her father had died just before she was born. Neither of the girls would know that they had a twin sister.

Jock's Kitchen provided all the meals for the schools in the area. It also served as a useful calendar of school holidays. If a mother was ever in doubt when her infant swore blind that there was no school on a particular day, the mother had only to step out of her house and sniff the air. The smell from Jock's Kitchen overpowered the aroma of the gasworks, animal skin store and refuse tip.

Rather like a 'Bisto' advert, the mother would sniff the air and say "Ah, Jock's Kitchen, off to school you lying little sod," as she kicked her offspring out the door.

Jock's Kitchen was located in the Capel Insh area of the Merkinch district. Close to Capel Insh lay the engine room of the whole area, Grant Street.

It was here that the real commerce of the area operated. It was in Grant Street that old men with coat collars turned up, and flat caps pulled down, scurried into the bookmakers clutching their betting slips, hoping that their wife was not in the area, and if she was, trying to avoid catching her eye, as the housekeeping money went to support the lifestyle of the bookmaker.

Still, it was not all bad news. It made a change from

investing the money in the pubs in the area.

The businesses in the Grant Street area, in addition to the bookmakers and Jock's Kitchen, included two public houses, a tobacconist's which specialised in snuff, a milk depot which dispensed milk from large churns into the customer's own jug, a hairdresser (where a haircut in film star style could be had for three-pence), a coal yard, a paraffin shop, a grocer, a baker, a scrap merchant, and two fish and chip shops. The diversity of outlets provided a good insight into the life-style of the community.

The horses operating the carts belonging to the refuse collectors, the rag-and-bone-men, the coal and milk distributors and the fresh fish delivery man (who happened to be John's granddad), were all stabled in a field close to Grant Street. The horses provided wonderful opportunities for the children to ride bareback, without the knowledge of the traders.

It was in one of the fish and chip shops in Grant Street that John, Sandy, and 'Sickly' Sidney Brown, made an unsuccessful induction into crime. The boys had been sent to the Grant Street chippie by their parents for the Friday night fish suppers, as the Ferry chippie was having a deep clean after catching fire. This happened at least once a month, and usually resulted in a queue of helpers, 'assisting' the chippie by taking away the fish suppers as smoke filled the van.

The lads' first venture into crime was executed reasonably well. It just lacked a bit of finesse. No, let us be honest. It lacked a lot of finesse.

The concept was simple. The boys had noticed that the shop owner had a tendency to leave bottles of lemonade on the servery counter. A plot was hatched. Laurel and Hardy accompanied by Goofy, alias John, Sandy, and Sidney, entered the chip shop. Sandy went to the counter to distract the attention of the owner by ordering the fish suppers, John grabbed a bottle. And they ran. 'Sickly', being rather a frail character, had to be dragged along being held up between John and Sandy, his feet six inches off the ground.

They stopped, breathless, about two hundred yards from the shop. There was no sign of pursuit and the boys laughed at the audacity and success of their scheme.

"Bags I go first," said John, feeling that he had done the dangerous bit.

"OK," replied Sandy "but just a wee slurp."

John took the screw top off the bottle and, ignoring Sandy's request about a wee slurp, gulped down some of the contents. His face curled up and with a shout of "Gudders, it's poison" he threw the bottle to the ground.

Two things happened simultaneously. As John threw the bottle to the ground it suddenly dawned on Sandy that he had ordered, and paid for, the fish suppers. But they had run from the shop before collecting them.

Five minutes later the boys returned to the shop, having rehearsed their grovelling piece. The boys toyed with the idea of telling the owner that they had chased the thief from the shop, and had retrieved the bottle for the owner. But, after a brief discussion, John and Sandy voted that Sidney should go back to the shop on his own. This resulted in a flood of tears from Sidney. The boys then agreed that honesty was the best policy. They all returned to the shop.

The fish shop owner took it in his stride. This had been the fifth such incident that week. He took delight in placing the bottles of vinegar in places accessible to the toe-rags who used the shop. He was already making enquiries about the availability of a clear poison, which could be put in the bottle instead of vinegar.

Handing the fish suppers to the boys he passed the comment, "I bet you three go to the 'Kessie' school. A word of advice. Forget the master criminal course. You three are headed for the nut-house."

Chapter Seven

One by one, fear on their faces, the adults approached the tree and, praying softly, proceeded to tie a piece of cloth to the tree. The annual pilgrimage to The Clootie Well was underway. Buses full of believers visited the well once a year and threw a coin in the Well, followed by the cloth-tree ritual. When the pilgrims tied the cloth to the tree John breathed a sigh of relief. If he had a sanity problem, it was a problem shared with half the town. John's doubts about his sanity had arisen the previous month, on the annual picnic to The Fairy Glen. Superstition had it that the Glen was occupied by fairies. John had his doubts about this, as apparently the fairies could only be seen during the summer months. He suggested to his mother that the fairies only used the Glen for holidays. Her look told him that she was beginning to have serious doubts about his sanity. He was ten years of age and he still believed in fairies.

Picnic trips were taken to the Black Isle on the ferryboat Eilean Dubh. The smell of diesel on the boat usually resulted in some of the less resilient travellers being sick before the boat had even left Inverness.

The Black Isle was a ten minute boat ride across the estuary of the Beauly Firth. John would sit on the banks of the Firth or play on the rocky beach, eating his jam or fish paste sandwiches, and look at his home on the opposite bank.

The men on the picnic filled in their time in the

traditional Inverness way, by spending several hours in the local tavern.

The Kessock Inn was located on the Inverness side of the firth, with the White House Inn on the Black Isle side. It was not unusual for some of the menfolk to spend all day in the Kessock Inn and, at the end of the day, board the Ferry, believing they were on their way back to Inverness, having forgotten that they had never left there in the first place. As the last ferry departed just after the inn closed, more than one husband found himself gazing across the Firth, wondering why the Ferry district was on the wrong side of the Firth, and why his family were waving to him from the other side of the water.

In the midst of the waving hands a clenched fist would appear and a wifely voice muttered "wait till I get you home you daft idiot."

The crossing to the Black Isle was not without incident. On one occasion a fracas erupted when the cry went up "man overboard." The boat was quickly brought to a stop as the crew, and curious passengers, rushed to the side of the boat to see who had fallen overboard.

In the process of throwing the lifebelt overboard the belt struck Mrs Fraser (Betty's mother) on the head. She turned round, not knowing what had happened. On seeing Mrs Ross (Tommy's mother), standing behind her, Mrs Fraser assumed that Mrs Ross had been the instigator of the blow. There was still some bad feeling from the Sports Day fiasco.

The end result was that, by the time the crew had pulled Mrs Ross and a tailor's dummy of a small child out of the water, the dummy missing two legs and an arm, all the passengers had taken sides. The Highland Constabulary made their daily visit to the Ferry. Whilst the constabulary were separating the feuding parties, John, who sat observing the action whilst munching his jam sandwich, casually picked up the discarded dummy body parts. He now had a complete dummy.

Easter was celebrated with services in all the local churches. For the younger children the joy of Easter lay in rolling hard-boiled, cochineal painted eggs down the brae at Inverness Castle. They then proceeded to eat the smashed egg, relishing the flavour, even though the coloured dye had seeped through the eggshell.

In August of each year Inverness emptied, as the town residents flocked to the nearby coastal town of Nairn using whatever form of transport was available. Horse and cart, train, bus, car, cycling or even walking. The Nairn Games was on, and this meant a day of festivities.

The main attraction for the children was the fun fair and the thrill of dodgem-cars, ghost trains and side stalls. The fortune-teller provided the big attraction for the women-folk, hoping for a glimpse, or a promise, of better things to come. For most of them, a husband who came home sober on payday would have been a wonderful start. In the meantime the men-folk were in the bars of Nairn rehearsing for payday.

The main objective of The Nairn Games was the athletic competition taking part on the adjacent links. The Inverness visitors were so taken by the fun fair and the local pubs that many of them did not even know that there was an athletic meeting being held in the adjoining field.

Chapter Eight

The announcement in a local newspaper stating that John's parents had been allocated a new council house was received with joy in the Urquhart household.

A major improvement was about to be made to the living conditions of the Urquhart family.

It was 1948 and The Inverness Housing Department had decided, in its wisdom, that the family was large enough, and respectable enough, to be allocated a three bedroom house in a new council estate in Dalneigh, a part of the town hitherto undeveloped.

The crucial element in the allocation however was that the family could afford to pay the rent. With John's father elder brother and two sisters working, the family was in a better financial position than most. They could afford a move. If not up-market, then certainly to a larger house.

The allocation of the new council houses was announced in the local press to show that a fair allocation system was in operation. For those named it was the equivalent of winning the pools.

The newspapers were eagerly scanned on publication by those wishing to know if they had been allocated a new home, and by those already allocated one, eager to know who their new neighbours would be. To John's delight Sandy Roberts' family had also been allocated a new house.

To accomplish the move John's father borrowed a lorry from his employers. It was with intense excitement that the boys in the family loaded household effects onto the back of the open lorry. The furniture consisted of a sideboard, a fold up bed-settee, two armchairs, a kitchen table, a cupboard, four kitchen chairs, two double beds, two wardrobes, and some multi-coloured scatter rugs made out of cloth remnants. All of the items were second or third hand. Boxes containing crockery and light bulbs removed from their sockets, sat alongside the lino they had removed from the floor. They were in no position to be charitable to the incoming occupants of their old home.

John's sisters had gone ahead to the new house to prepare the house for the arrival of the furniture. There was little to prepare however as the house was brand new. On the back of the lorry the boys were nearly wetting themselves with excitement, counting the house numbers as they drove along the street.

To a shout of "We're there" from the youngest child, the lorry screeched to a halt. John's cry, as he fell from the back of the lorry, was stifled by the roll of linoleum which landed on top of him.

By the time the boys arrived at the house the curtains had been put in place. Tea and sandwiches awaited. The rest of the day was spent by the grown-ups unloading and unpacking, and having intense discussions on who slept where, and with whom.

Meanwhile the younger children began to explore the wonders of their new playing areas, particularly the potential in a building site.

The provision of open coal fires to two of the bedrooms was the icing on the cake as far as John's mother and the children were concerned. The coalbunker was located in the back garden. This had its drawbacks, particularly during the winter months. It was never much fun having to clear inches of snow from the bunker.

The fires in the bedrooms were banked up every night in the winter but, despite the fire, the clothing on the bed, and the brick hot water bottle, Jack Frost still made his appearance in the middle of the night, leaving behind icy windows and frozen bodies. The open fields in front of the house gave no protection from the winds sweeping in from the North.

For John's father the biggest asset was the large garden. From the day of arrival, he began to cultivate the garden into vegetable, lawn and floral areas. His first task was to plant a lilac bush at the front of the house, as this was John's mother's favourite plant.

The garden shed was a source of great enjoyment for John. It contained all manner of items he had never seen before, and had no idea what they could be used for. When the shed was locked he always knew that there was something special stored in there. This could have been a second-hand tricycle, bought at a jumble sale, lovingly repainted and with the addition of a pump, or a pedal car, transformed from red to blue, waiting to be given to one of the children as a birthday present.

Dalneigh was an area of wide open spaces. These spaces later developed into the remainder of the new estate, but John's initial impression was that he was in paradise. He had even forgotten about up-market West Drive. Even the Dalneigh street names, such as Laurel Avenue and Hawthorn Drive, sounded more up-market than the Ferry streets.

John's new route to the Kessock School involved a walk along a tree-lined lane which saw very little daylight. It was not unusual to see a clutch of children, on their way home from school, rush out of Bumbers Lane in the early dark of a winter's evening, as though the Devil himself was chasing them. John was not sure which route he considered safer. The Devil route or the Harbour Inn pirate route.

In 1951 an air of excitement swept through the street in which John lived. A Morris family saloon car, with English occupants, had broken down outside John's house. The appearance on the estate of a dustcart, milk float, horse-drawn cart or coal lorry was routine. But a car was still a rare occurrence. A car, containing foreigners, actually breaking down on the street, heralded The Second Coming.

Within two minutes of the car stopping it was surrounded by John and six of his friends, plus a few grown-ups. It was quickly established that the occupants of the vehicle were on a tour of the Highlands.

John's father quickly took command of the situation by looking under the bonnet of the car. John was then instructed to go to the nearest garage to find a mechanic. In the meantime 'The English' were invited to tea and clootie dumpling by John's parents.

'The English' looked at the clootie dumpling suspiciously, probably fearing it was a reprisal for Culloden. John was bewildered. These people were foreigners, yet his parents were entertaining them.

On returning with the mechanic John was given half a crown for his trouble. He must have been easily corruptible in those days as his feelings towards the English changed immediately. This was his first encounter with any foreigners. They were not as odd as he had expected, although they spoke English with a strange accent.

At the age of eleven John took up employment as a paperboy at the local newsagent at a pay of two shillings a week. He was allowed to read all the comics he wanted. He could not believe his luck.

The luck came to an end however when the newsagent, and irate customers, decided that John's practice of taking the comics home to read, was not acceptable. John realised that they may have accepted a delay in delivery of an hour or two, but six different comics and The Children's Newspaper in one day took a lot of reading. Delivery was sometimes a day later than it should have been.

The loss of the free toys provided with *The Topper* and *The Beezer* was also an issue. But as far as John was concerned, the smile from his friends on receiving the gifts was sufficient compensation for the telling off he received from both his father and the newsagent.

Overlooking Dalneigh, across the Caledonian Canal, the twin hills of Craig Dunain and Craig Phadrig were a great source of play for the youngsters, particularly in an area known as The Lions' Gates. The rocks and the caves in this area lent themselves to war games.

Sometimes the games were taken too seriously, however. On one occasion in a derelict farmhouse a game of cowboys and indians was in full swing, with the cowboys trapped in the farmhouse. One of the indian squaws, Violet MacDonald, decided to help in the eviction proceedings by applying a flaming torch to the farmhouse structure. The fire brigade saw little humour in the situation, but more humour than the defeated cowboys, two of them having run home crying their eyes out. The farmhouse was burnt to the ground.

John was reaching the conclusion that the women in Inverness were more dangerous than the men. The local psychiatric hospital was located on Craig Dunain, and he could already identify three potential female patients, all under the age of eleven.

It was at the age of twelve that John found what he

believed to be the perfect weapon for the War Games. His father had returned from Burma with a Ghurkha kukri. The kukri was kept in a linen closet in the house. John frequently examined the kukri and speculated on how many people had been killed with it. His father had already advised him not to touch it, and had stressed to him that once a Ghurkha kukri was drawn legend dictated that blood must also be drawn.

Each street had its own gang, the ages of the members ranging from eight to fourteen. On one bright sunny day John was assembled with his gang. They had just completed building a gang-hut from materials 'borrowed' from the builder's yard.

John stood there with the rest of his gang and explained about the kukri and the legend that went with it.

The war game started and John charged towards the Jap lines. There was total panic. Children ran everywhere, with Sandy Roberts' voice louder than the rest, clearly screaming, "Johnny Urquhart's gone mad, send for the police."

By the time the grown ups had arrived, John had thrown the kukri into the canal. His father never found out where his war trophy had disappeared to.

It was normal practice for one gang to set alight an opposing gang's bonfire several days before Guy Fawkes night. Bonfires would be built out of building materials, which were stored behind a locked compound, with only a six foot fence to safeguard it. Fortunately for those who borrowed the materials the builder's storekeeper had been taught at the 'Kessie'. He could not quite grasp the concept of stock-control.

The premature setting alight of bonfires would usually result in tears and tantrums. This was from the parents. The boys simply vowed to get revenge, in whatever shape or form they could.

On bonfire night potatoes were stolen from a neighbour's garden. The potatoes were baked in the bonfire. The bonfire was suitably topped with an effigy of Hitler or the villain of the day. Fabulous fireworks, with names like Golden Rain, Mighty Atom, Snow Showers and Crackerjacks would fill the sky.

News of a wedding in the town would be swiftly communicated from child to child as the prospect of a 'scramble' arose. This was the tradition of a father throwing coins to the children as he left the family home with his daughter on her way to get married. Being confronted by a dozen or more 'scramblers' was enough for any father to dig deep into his pocket for a handful of change.

In 1950 John's father received a turkey as a Christmas bonus from his employers. For the first time ever the family sat down to a real Christmas dinner. The fact that the family was split between the kitchen and the living room did not spoil the festivities. The living room was decked with paper chains, holly and mistletoe. Paper balls hung from the clothes-pulley in the kitchen. The children made their own Christmas cards and crackers, with each cracker containing a sweet. A Christmas tree, with lights, provided the final touch to a memorable Christmas for John and his family.

Christmas presents for the children consisted of an apple, sweets, crayons and a drawing book, placed in each child's stocking, which hung at the end of the shared bed. A combined Christmas Day and Birthday meant John received more presents than his brothers or sisters.

By the mid 1950s the longed-for presents for the women-folk was a box of chocolates, as large as possible, with an appealing picture on the front. The type of chocolates was less important than the box. The ribbon from the chocolate box would be put away, for use as hair-bands at a later date. The chocolate box lid, with a one penny calendar attached, would form an attractive wall decoration.

This was why the picture on the box was so important. Nothing was wasted.

The men, on receipt of the desired present of a packet of fifty or one hundred cigarettes, would transfer the cigarettes into an obligatory cigarette case, which served as a status symbol to their peers. An essential accoutrement to the cigarette case was a petrol-filled lighter. This would, on occasions, burst into flames, usually at the critical moment when an eager paramour, out to impress, lit a cigarette for the intended love of his life. Having her eyebrows singed was not the biggest turn-on in the world.

Weekly credit was a way of life for all families. Credit was always on a payday to payday basis. Further credit would not be granted if there was an outstanding bill. Brooke Bond Dividend stamps worth one penny each were saved. A complete book worth five shillings was a valuable source of income.

Ration coupons had to be presented for food and clothing until the mid-fifties, when all rationing was lifted. There were no supermarkets. Each item purchased had to be picked from the shelf by the shop assistant, then wrapped, and then handed over to the customer.

To supplement the grocery budget mothers would make bread, cakes, puddings and sweets. There was always fierce competition from the children to be the one to wipe their finger around the bowl used for making a vanilla sponge or fairy cakes. Tins of Nestlés Condensed Milk, used for making Swiss tablet, were fought over to get the last drop of the sickly sweet contents. Rock cakes to break your teeth on. Jam tarts so fresh that they burnt your tongue. Rhubarb dipped in sugar. Clootie Dumplings and roly poly pudding. John's mother never seemed to stop baking, to the sound of music from 'Housewives Choice'. She always seemed to have traces of flour on her apron and in her hair.

Door to door credit selling was provided by a trader known as 'The Star Bootman'. John never did discover why this name was given, but assumed it was because this particular salesman was the main source of clothing and footwear for the families who lived in the area. Avoiding the 'Star Bootman' when money was tight was a regular occurrence

Electricity was controlled from a shilling-in-the-slot meter. It was standard practice to place a few one shilling pieces on top of the meter each payday. Candles were always kept readily available. Just in case.

Fresh fish was provided to the Ferry and Dalneigh estates by John's grandfather, with the call "herring, fresh herring" as he trawled the streets with his horse and cart. On occasions his grandfather would allow John to sit in the driving seat of the cart and 'gee up' the horse along the road. His grandfather's presence on the street was welcomed by those seeking fresh fish. There was an even bigger queue for the manure droppings. There were very few families who did not grow their own vegetables.

Summer days were spent on the banks of the Caledonian Canal, chasing butterflies, or collecting raspberries and blackcurrants, which John's mother would turn into jam.

Fishing from the end of a jetty at Clachnaharry, risking life and limb for the pleasure of catching a few tiddlers, all of which were thrown back into the water, was great fun. The jetty stretched about fifty feet into the firth and was constructed of what appeared to be rotting timber. In order to get close enough to fish with string and safety pin, the children had to clamber down eight feet, via a seaweed covered pole. It was a miracle that none of them ended up in the water. All this risk to catch a fish smaller than the worm on the end of the safety pin which served as a hook.

Almost anything would be collected. Even cardboard milk bottle tops had an appeal. They served no useful purpose. But the challenge on who could collect the most was there. The important thing about collecting was that it gave ownership of something.

When John was twelve 'Sickly' Sydney Brown was admitted to hospital. It was Christmas time. John and Sandy visited Sidney, taking with them their best wishes and a request that Sidney tell his mother to release his football to the boys. This was the only real leather football the Laurel Avenue gang had, and was the main reason for the hospital visit. It was not that John or Sandy did not care about Sidney, but football was a much higher priority.

The hospital visit turned out to be eventful, however, as John was exposed to the sight of attractive young uniformed nurses for the first time. He vowed that he would marry a nurse one day. Or at the very least have a nurse as a girlfriend.

It was whilst John was having these thoughts that he experienced a burning sensation in his loins. He called to a passing nurse. "Help me nurse, my willie's on fire."

The nurse, having never experienced this complaint before, sought the help of the much older Ward Sister.

The Ward Sister looked at John, and saw the gleam in his eyes. A gleam she had last seen some thirty years before, at the local dance hall, when she was being chatted up by a spotty faced youth. She quickly brought herself back down to earth as she recalled the particular evening. She suddenly realised that she was smiling.

The young nurse, having never seen the Sister smile before, thought she was having a spasm, and began to scream. This awoke the, by now, panting Sister.

Embarrassed, she looked at John.

"Right", she said, "drop your trousers." Again she was reminded of the spotty youth.

John obliged.

The Sister took one look.

"I know how to fix that," she said.

One minute later John had a needle thrust into his backside.

He looked down at his willie. It had shrunk. The throbbing sensation had stopped.

"By heavens," John stated "that's effective stuff."

Whilst all this was happening the snow was falling outside, as a reminder to all of the festive season.

The hospital ward was festooned and a giant Christmas tree stood at the entrance to the ward. Underneath the tree presents were scattered, ready for distribution around the ward on Christmas Day.

It was Christmas morning before the nursing staff realised that two of the presents were missing. Subsequent enquiries revealed that, whilst a young visitor at Sidney Brown's bedside was being treated for 'a personal reason not connected to a medical condition', a second young visitor had been seen leaving the hospital with items stuffed under his jacket.

The lads from the Ferry had transferred their skills to Dalneigh.

There was a bonus for John that particular Christmas Day Birthday. In addition to his 'present' from the hospital (which turned out to be a girl's doll), he received the book 'Treasure Island' from his parents. John wondered if the pirates from 'Treasure Island' had ever used The Harbour Inn.

These were days when school holidays seemed to last forever, the summers were long and hot and the winters cold and bitter.

But there was always time for mischief.

But, despite the mischievousness, these were days of innocence.

Chapter Nine

Slimey Jefferson smiled as the headmaster pulled the wan looking lad into the classroom. Slimey had deliberately engineered his main teaching duties to be in charge of the Grade C pupils, the thickest in the school, and, at the age of eleven, just right for a regular beating. The class had a reputation for misbehaviour. This allowed Slimey to indulge in his fantasies.

"Urquhart," he said, "I'm glad you could join us."

He remembered Urquhart from the lad's first year in the infant school. Somehow Urquhart had always managed to avoid him, by being constantly in classes not taught by Slimey. But Urquhart had not been concentrating on his work lately, and the headmaster had felt that a few weeks in Mr Jefferson's class would help Urquhart to concentrate in the run-up to examination time.

Slimey recalled the incident with the hand-bell. He had always been convinced that Urquhart had been the brains behind the idea. He was not fooled by the quiet demeanour of Urquhart. He knew a troublemaker when he saw one.

The school term had only four weeks to run, and the departure of the hooligans to a school of higher education. Slimey cringed at this thought. A brain transplant would not improve the intelligence of this rabble.

The end of the final year at the 'Kessie' brought with it the dreaded ritual of the school dance. This included learning the intricacies of The Gay Gordons, The Dashing

White Sergeant and The Military Two Step.

The pupils were assembled in the school hall, with the girls on one side and the boys on the other side, being cajoled by the teachers to take a partner. John could see that, although there were several good-looking girls there, the midwife at his birth would be in for some serious competition in the years ahead.

He was dressed in a clean pair of short trousers, a white shirt borrowed from a neighbour, and a pair of socks that clung to his ankles despite the piece of string attempting to keep the socks to knee level. His shoes were polished and for once had no holes.

John had a moment of panic when Miss Rawlings, the games teacher, grabbed him and commanded that he dance with her. He made his apologies, on the grounds that he was not allowed to dance because he had a broken foot. Miss Rawlings looked at him in surprise. She later looked at him in annoyance when she saw him on the dance floor with Susan Simpson, another of the Ferry kids. John had held a soft spot for Susan since the age of four after the 'Wee Willie MacDonald' incident in Craigton Avenue. It was the first time that he had ever seen his soul mate in a clean dress, and without a runny nose. He was totally smitten.

This was John's last term at the 'Kessie'. He gave no consideration whatsoever to the possible repercussions for his younger brothers who were also at the school.

In the final year of primary school the pupils were asked to specify which course of education they wished to follow. The route they would ultimately take would be dictated by their exam results.

John opted for the 'Commercial' course at the local High School. Sandy, who had ambitions to be an Engineer, opted for a 'Technical Course' at the High School. Neither of the boys considered applying for the Academy. The Academy was located up the hill. The thought of visiting the hill district was daunting.

But whilst John and Sandy were heading for the High School, Susan Simpson (John's soul-mate and Dux of the 'Kessie'), and Irene Norman (the animal tormentor), were destined for the higher echelons of the Academy.

In John's final week at the 'Kessie', Miss Goodall, in her first year as a teacher, was standing in for Slimey Jefferson, who was on holiday.

How foolish it was to put an inexperienced and short-sighted teacher in charge of any class in which John was a pupil became evident on the final day of the term.

Miss Goodall was, by the fourth day, getting close to a breakdown, but she was mollified by the fact that John Urquhart, contrary to expectations, was behaving himself remarkably well. Not only was John well behaved, but the new pupil in the seat next to him was also remarkably quiet.

Miss Goodall looked at her watch. One more hour and she would be free.

A shout from the rear of the class brought her back down to earth. John Urquhart seemed to be having a disagreement with the quiet child in the adjoining seat. Miss Goodall moved forward to remonstrate, just as John hit the other child a savage blow to the head.

Miss Goodall's face dropped. Open-mouthed, she looked at the bloody head rolling about the floor.

She ran from the classroom screaming, "Let me out. Let me out."

As soon as she had left the room John picked up the tailor's dummy from the floor. He wiped clean the tomato ketchup, and ran from the classroom, taking with him the dummy.

The headmaster's investigation revealed that Miss Goodall had entered the classroom that morning with her cross in the upside down position. Her story about headless pupils made no sense.

A reminder was issued to all teachers on the correct method of holding the cross.

Chapter Ten

With over 1000 pupils the High School was split into two streams. The Junior Secondary Stream offered a three year course, designed to prepare pupils for the outside world at the age of fifteen. The Senior Secondary Stream provided a five year course, preparing for further education to university entry level. John and Sandy were enrolled into the Senior stream. Their career prospects were looking bright.

The good news for the boys was that the High School was much closer to their homes. Even better news was the fact that it had five schoolhouses competing in sporting events. This, John theorised, greatly increased his chances of getting into one of the school football teams. But, for John, the best news was still to come. In his first year Commercial class of thirty-five pupils, only five were boys.

This statistic turned out to be of little significance however, as all the girls in the Commercial Stream made it quite clear that any young lad intent on an office career must be a bit weird. Men were meant to do manly things.

John's first week at High School, at the age of twelve, was a nightmare.

He was the only lad at school in short trousers.

His mother advised him that the 'Star Bootman' would take at least a week to deliver a pair of trousers, assuming that there was sufficient credit. This caused some anxiety for John. Not the absence of long trousers, but the fact that his mother was going to speak to the 'Star Bootman'.

When the salesman had called at the house for his money the previous week, John had been sent to the door to say his parents were not in. Watching from the bedroom window, his mother did not hear John explain to the salesman that his parents were not available, as they were in hospital, both critically ill with malaria. The salesman walked away from the house shaking his head, muttering "poor souls."

The lack of long trousers resolved itself however. John shared a bedroom with his eldest brother James, who had four pairs of long trousers. Six inches chopped off the bottom of one pair and nobody realised that John wore his brother's long trousers to school for a week.

John's week was complete when he found two shillings and a packet of five Woodbines in his brother's pocket. John did not want the cigarettes, but he could trade them.

A few days later John heard his brother remark to his mother that his best pair of trousers was missing. The mystery was never solved. But James was convinced that John was involved in the disappearance.

When the 'Star Bootman' arrived at the house, at the request of John's mother, the salesman remarked on how well she looked. John's father overheard the conversation, and thinking it was a chat up line at his wife, threw the salesman out the door.

John was at school when the form teacher advised the pupils of the death of King George VI. The pupils were devastated, to the extent that one of the girls put her arms around John and sobbed. He quite enjoyed the experience, and looked forward to some more bad news. He tried to imagine who could be older and more important than the King, and who may have a short life expectancy.

Unfortunately nobody came to mind.

John's hopes that on joining the High School he would easily slot into one of the house football teams did not come to fruition. During the four years at High School he was always down as a reserve. It was in the December of 1953, in the middle of a blizzard, that he turned out for his house in the final of the inter-house football competition. John's team won the game by six goals to nil and he scored.

Well, almost scored.

He was slapped on the back by his team-mates when he appeared to score a goal from two yards out at the height of the blizzard. There were no goal nets. John decided not to tell his team-mates that the ball had gone the wrong side of the post. Moments of glory for him were few and far between.

John's father was amazed when John told him that he had played in the winning side in a cup final, and had scored a goal. He omitted to tell his father that the goal was dubious and that due to the heavy snow only eight players had turned up for the other team.

During the final year at the High School pupils in the Junior Stream were allowed time away from school to participate in 'tattie howking', the practice of helping farmers to get in their potato stock. Pupils in the Senior Stream classes were denied the opportunity of taking part in this activity and the chance to earn some money. This did not make it any easier for families of some of the Senior Stream pupils. Every extra penny income contributed greatly to the household budget.

It was probably just as well that John was unable to participate in the 'tattie howking'. He was the classic seven-stone weakling, the type seen in the Charles Atlas commercials. He would probably have been shown up by all the girls.

John's score with the girls, despite the thirty to five ratio, was still a great big fat zero. By this time he had developed his own personality (or to be more precise lack of personality). He was small for his age, bespectacled, quietly serious and open to bullying. He remembered the praise from his neighbour shortly after his birth, on how beautiful a baby he had been whilst wearing his gas mask. He debated with himself as to whether getting a gas mask would improve his chances with the girls.

He attempted to take out one of the less attractive girls. She was overweight and spotty but, he thought, worth a try.

He was rebuffed on the grounds that "she never went out with boys who wore glasses."

He retorted that "they would need to be blind before they took her out."

She replied "that her body was her temple."

He replied that "because of her size she must mean the Taj Mahal."

She replied by hitting him across the face.

He was rescued by the PE teacher who took him to task for picking on girls. John was placed on detention for four hours.

The following week the school announced that students on the Senior Secondary Stream could apply for a science course. John's enquiry, as to whether there was a course available on sexual chemistry, was ignored.

Sandy, who was marginally more macho than John, was experiencing the same problems.

Girlfriends were in short supply.

Chapter Eleven

It was a cold wet miserable evening, in November 1953, when the Drill Sergeant for the Army Cadet Force raised his eyes from his copy of Tit-Bits, to check on the activities on the firing range. The usual crowd of lads had turned up with two new recruits. The Drill Sergeant yawned. It had been a hard week at the tannery and he was glad it was Friday night. "Get this crowd out of the way", he mused, "and straight down to the British Legion Club for a few pints."

He pulled out a packet of Kensitas cigarettes and carefully extracted one, folding away the five gift coupons. Another twenty coupons and he could get a set of whisky glasses. Drinking out of jam jars had lost its appeal for him. He actually did not mind too much. But his girlfriend, Mrs Mary Wilson, from The Harbour Inn, was beginning to get airs and graces.

He lowered his head, and then sharply raised it again. He blinked, as it dawned on him that one of the new recruits was wandering across the firing range. There was no danger, no ammunition, but he had repeatedly stressed to the recruits never to walk in front of a weapon.

He was aware that he was in a state of shock when the matchstick burnt his finger.

Leaping to his feet he yelled at the top of his voice.

"You stupid sod, get off the firing range."

John had never been spoken to in such a manner before. Well certainly not since his Kessock School days.

John decided, there and then, never to have anything to do with the Army. He looked around for a youth organisation more deserving of his talent.

He dismissed the Boys' Club on the grounds that there was little opportunity of meeting girls there. The Boy Scouts was also dismissed as being too elitist and full of Academy pupils. He applied to join the Y.W.C.A. but was turned down on the grounds that it was an organisation for girls. He appealed against this decision, but was still rejected.

John was so desperate to do so something, to be part of something, that he volunteered as a Sunday School teacher at his local church. He had no idea what this involved, but Moira, the minister's attractive daughter, was a Sunday School teacher. John was willing to go to any lengths.

Each Sunday John would hand out coloured stickers to the Sunday School class for 'good behaviour'. He was at a loss to understand what bad behaviour children could possibly get up to in a Sunday School.

But this was still not enough to keep his mind occupied.

John stood proudly in front of the mirror, adjusting his pillbox hat on which the metal figure 12 gleamed. He had carefully put blanco on his stripes, and on his crossover-webbing strap. He looked the part.

The boys had enlisted in the company attached to the local church. The company was desperate for members, and as John was the oldest member on joining he was immediately made a Sergeant. He was also asked to captain the football team. The Boys Brigade had clearly not heard of John's previous military, or sporting, ability.

John held the football captaincy for one year, during which time the team managed to lose every game in spectacular fashion.

At the beginning of his second season as football captain the officers in the Company came to their senses. They offered to help John in team selection. The following Friday evening, between drill and the first aid lesson, the team for the next game was announced. John was down as first reserve. The team won by six goals to two, and went on to have a respectable season.

John took part in three games that season, always being substituted in the last ten minutes, when victory was secure, or defeat inevitable.

Annual Summer camp for the Inverness Battalion of The Boys Brigade was held at Carrbridge, a small village some thirty miles from Inverness, at the foot of the Cairngorm Mountains. These camps provided the only holiday for most of the boys.

As two of the senior boys, John and Sandy, along with thirty other members of the Brigade, reported to Carrbridge the day before the arrival of the main party. The senior boys had responsibility for setting up the tents and preparing the site. Lorries left Inverness laden with all manner of camping equipment to the sound of the boys singing "Blow the good old bugles boys and give a hearty cheer, while we are camping at Carrbridge."

The arrival at Carrbridge of the two hundred boys in the main party resulted in a march from the railway station to the campsite headed by a pipe-band. There was always a tremendous reception by the local community, fronted by a dozen of the local girls, and the owner of the village sweet shop. The noise of the reception party was matched by the sighs of relief from Inverness as the parents of the boys who were at camp settled back for a week of peace and quiet.

With tent inspections and bed-packs, there was a quasi-military feel about the camp. For John, this was all a wonderful experience.

For the first time ever John felt that he really belonged to something. It was a happy time in his life.

Chapter Twelve

Inverness closed down on Sundays as residents went to church services, or simply recovered from another normal drunken Saturday night. Those with sufficient energy either strolled around the town shopping centre, promenaded around the Ness Islands, or played pitch and putt, although the latter pastime tended to be for the rich kids from the Hill District.

They were all seeking excitement. But there was none to be found.

It was on one such Sunday in 1955 that John, Sandy, Billy Saunders, Sidney Brown and Alex Todd gathered together in one of the few establishments open in Inverness on a Sunday – a coffee bar. They met there every Sunday to discuss the previous day's football results, and generally put the world to right.

The fact that the owner of the cafe had an extremely attractive daughter was a bonus.

This particular Sunday turned out a little bit different.

The boys found themselves in an intense discussion on the pros and cons of marriage. At the age of sixteen they felt they knew enough about life to debate this issue. The discussion had been prompted by the news that one of their school friends had become engaged.

The boys reached the conclusion that marriage, at any age, was an insane step to take, regardless of the circumstances.

The end result of two hours discussion during which

time they consumed a variety of coffees and ice-cream sodas served by the goddess, (all to no avail – the daughter of the house clearly had more taste in men than they realised), was that they took a vow that none of them would ever get married. In the event that one of them was to break this very solemn oath he would pay to the other four the sum of five pounds.

The oath was duly written out and signed by all. They each retained a copy.

John was not to know that this particular piece of paper would play an important part in his life, many years later, and some eight thousand miles from Inverness. Nor was he to know that one of the signatories would be dead within a few years.

Chapter Thirteen

In 1953 there was consternation in the Western Isles when rumours spread that Scotland was part of a black republic. The concern arose when a visit by the Queen of Tonga to Inverness coincided with the annual pilgrimage of the licensed victuallers from Stornoway. The publicans were surprised at how black the Queen was, as she had looked white at her Coronation. They attributed this to the experimental television reception they were receiving in Stornoway at the time. They had visited Inverness in the belief that Queen Elizabeth was visiting there. They were clearly in some sort of time warp, as the two royal visits were months apart.

When Queen Elizabeth visited the town as part of her Coronation tour of the UK she was met by jubilant crowds lining the streets. School children stood on the roadside, waving their council-issued Union Flags. Each child was presented with a Coronation Mug. Every product that could be printed upon was emblazoned with pictures of the Queen. Items as diverse as teapots, chocolates and even penknives bore the royal image. Pride of place in many households was a four inch replica Royal Coach which was placed on the mantelpiece. The Coronation was big business.

Part of the Coronation celebrations included a torch relay from John O'Groats to Lands End. John was asked to participate in this, but thought the distance of eight hundred odd miles would probably be too much for him.

Nevertheless, in a spirit of willingness, he advised the organisers that he would take part. At long last somebody appeared to be recognising his sporting ability.

He had however misunderstood the assignment. The youth organisations in the town were taking part in a national relay. John and Sandy ran a three mile stretch of road between Inverness and Nairn. John held the pseudo Olympic torch. The boys thought that they were participating in the Olympic Games.

A visit by Billy Graham, the American evangelist, brought forth thousands from all over the North of Scotland, all seeking to be converted. John went forward to be converted, but as he was a Sunday School teacher at the time this hardly compared to turning water into wine. Moira, the vicar's daughter, after whom John lusted, was converted at the same time as John.

On the way home to Dalneigh, whilst John was attempting to talk Moira into a walk through the romantic haunts of the Ness Islands, she advised John that she was so moved by the Billy Graham experience that she had decided to become a nun thus dashing John's hopes.

The visit of Billy Graham was the main subject of topic in the bars of Inverness during the following days. The converted sinners eventually returned to doing what they did best, drinking Scotland dry.

In August 1956 the Iowa State University Girls Pipe Band arrived in the town. Following a performance, attended by several hundred drooling youths, the girls were invited by the local Council to be guests of honour at a dance. John attended. It was his first encounter with females other than those of the Inverness variety. The American girls were friendlier than the local girls. This was probably due to the fact that they did not know John.

John contemplated a move to Iowa, or perhaps even

Hollywood to see Doris Day. He wondered if there were any prospects of work in America. He was brought down to earth by his eldest brother who, when John revealed his ambitions, stated that Mickey Mouse might need a stunt man. There was never any shortage of encouragement in the Urquhart household.

The American dance was successful however as John secured the telephone number of one of the girls. She made him promise to call her when she returned to the States. John was on a high. Suddenly his whole life had become that little bit more exciting.

Four weeks after the American dance John discovered the piece of paper on which the American girl had written her telephone number. Armed with a handful of loose change he used a call box and asked the operator to connect him with the American number.

A few minutes later the telephone rang at the other end. There was crackling and buzzing on the line, but the male American voice was clear enough.

"Federal Bureau of Investigation, can I help you?"

John replaced the receiver and wondered, not for the first time, if the world was full of sick women.

Between Billy Graham and the Iowa State University Girls Pipe Band, he had also experienced enough of Americans.

Apart from Doris Day, of course. He could never get enough of Doris.

Chapter Fourteen

Wearing an overcoat and suit that was two sizes too big, and a flat cap which rested on his spectacles, John looked like a teenage dirty old man.

At the age of sixteen he took the decision to leave school. This was not the most sensible of decisions as his school exams, which would determine whether he could go to university, were due to be held in the following weeks. His parents did their best to talk him out of this decision, but his mind was set.

The decision was prompted by the affluence of most of his friends who had started their first job and who could afford to do the things that John wanted to do. Job vacancies were rare however, particularly for young lads seeking an office career. He was fortunate in that, within days of reaching his decision to leave, he secured a position as an office junior at a local newspaper.

In order to prepare him for his new role at work John's father took him to a local tailor. John was fitted out with a two piece suit, raincoat, cap and black shoes. The wearing of a flat cap by lads in their teens was quite common. His father bought the items on credit on payments of half-a-crown a week. The items were purchased two sizes larger than required. "To allow for growth" John's father explained.

One week after leaving school he commenced work at *The Northern Gazette*. The newspaper focussed on local farming news and the stock market (cattle as opposed to money). The office was Dickensian in character, with tall sloping desks and high-backed chairs. John estimated the average age of the office staff to be about one hundred and three.

From his first week's wages of twelve shillings and sixpence John bought chocolates and the record 'The Rock and Roll Waltz for his parents. The following week he was asked to contribute five shillings towards the cost of a record player. He had overlooked the fact that they had no means of playing the record.

The main aspect of his job was to carry out filing and other routine office junior tasks. There was one area in which he had specific responsibility however, and that was to handle replies to Box Number advertisements.

A simple task one would have thought.

The newspaper had made the mistake of assuming John had a semblance of common sense. There was no doubting John's intelligence. He just read too much into things, with the result that, inevitably, complications arose.

The main objective in using a Box Number is to maintain confidentiality.

John was in his new job only two weeks when an advertisement was placed in the newspaper stating, 'Trained mental nurse with daughter aged 18 seeks apartment and board, will provide references and service. Apply Box No 1223'.

A week later a request to place an advertisement was handed to John, stating 'Farmer, aged 43, recently widowed, seeks female company with view to relationship'.

John immediately recalled the plea from the nurse, and forwarded the details of the nurse direct to the farmer. He saw no point in retaining the confidentiality when two people were so clearly suited.

It transpired that the lonely farmer had a history of mental illness, and was under suspicion of murdering his wife. The farmer was a patient of the accommodation-seeking nurse who had, in the preceding few weeks, complained to the police about sexual advances from the farmer.

The police had to intervene when the farmer began visiting the nurse daily, seeking to take up her offer of 'services'.

Within four weeks of taking up employment as an office junior John was promoted to the position of tea-boy with the comment "If you want to be a social worker join the Church. Preferably in Africa."

John no longer had responsibility for Box Numbers.

Three months after joining *The Gazette* he resigned.

Chapter Fifteen

Sandy took the decision to leave school eight months after John. It was with some enthusiasm that he commenced work with an engineering company as a trainee surveyor. The company was employed in the erection of electricity poles throughout the Highlands, bringing power to remote communities. Sandy had visions of planning and plotting. This was to be his first step on the road to be an engineer.

As part of his cold weather clothing he was provided with a duffle coat. Sandy took to wearing this regularly as it gave him a feeling of rugged manliness. He quickly noticed that girls would give him furtive looks and this excited him.

He never did find out what the word 'nerd' meant.

During the following twelve months he spent most days working as a chain-boy. This involved pulling a fifty foot long chain, sometimes over rough and snowy terrain, and then holding up a measuring pole so that the surveyor could, using a theodolite, plot the route of the power lines.

One day a week was spent in the office, when Sandy would plot the graphs, based on the surveyor's report, for issue to the erection team.

This was not without its problems.

On several occasions the foreman of the erection team had been heard to complain that the survey was incorrect. They quickly established the reason. At times during the surveys Sandy had dropped out of sight of the surveyor, because of the nature of the terrain. Every fifty feet Sandy would hold up the measuring pole and the surveyor would take a reading. When there was a particularly deep dip, Sandy would lift the measuring pole some two or three feet off the ground to assist the surveyor in his sighting. Sandy did not think to advise the surveyor of his actions.

This frequently resulted in the erection team, on turning up to execute work, finding that it was logistically impossible to follow the route planned without the proposed cables being closer to the ground than safety dictated.

On one task with the survey company Sandy assisted a surveyor in planning a power route to a village close to Loch Ness. This involved travelling alongside the loch on a single track road. It was November, the roads were icy, and disaster struck. On rounding a bend in the road they drove straight into a lorry coming from the opposite direction. Fortunately the weather conditions had meant that both vehicles were travelling at a sensible speed. The head-on collision was enough however to push the light van back to the edge of the loch, with the tail end hanging over the water.

Sandy was, by now, regretting not having resigned when the errors on the graphs had been discovered.

The surveyor he was with was Irish and Sandy had great difficulty understanding what he said. There were a couple of words which, if John had heard them, would not have gained a coloured sticker at the Sunday School, but the gist of it was "For Christ's sake, don't move."

Sandy could see that this was not the time to moralise on taking the name of The Lord in vain. Had either he, or the surveyor, moved out of the front of the van, it would have tipped into the water.

By this time, in order to establish how they could help, the occupants of the lorry had gathered at the front of the van.

Sandy had a moment of panic when he realised that the lorry was one belonging to the survey company, and the driver was the foreman who had wasted many valuable hours in abortive erections on following Sandy's graphs.

Their eyes met, recognition dawned on the foreman's face, and he smiled. Sandy was sure that the surveyor was tempted to leave the van hanging over the loch.

"Don't move," the foreman added to the voice of the surveyor. "You are just on the edge of the loch. The slightest movement and you will end up in twenty feet of Loch Ness."

The surveyor looked quizzically at the foreman.

"Right," continued the foreman. "Whilst we sit on the bonnet the heavier of the two of you should exit the van."

Two minutes later the surveyor was standing on dry land alongside the foreman.

Suddenly the foremen looked over Sandy's head. With pointed finger he shouted.

"Look lads, it's Nessie."

On hearing this, the two erectors raised their buttocks from the bonnet of the van and rushed alongside the foreman and surveyor, who by this time were also pointing excitedly.

"Oh! My God, it's getting closer!" the foreman declared.

Sandy began to panic. If he moved too quickly the van would topple into twenty feet of cold black Loch Ness. If he did not move quickly the monster would get him.

The foreman, surveyor and erectors all gesticulated for Sandy to stay still, at the same time giving a running commentary on the progress of the monster.

Sandy began to cry. How would he explain this to his parents who had insisted that he go to university? Would he ever see his parents again? He realised that he would probably be the first person to be eaten by the Loch Ness Monster.

The foreman dropped his arm. He spoke to the surveyor and the two erectors.

A minute later the four men began to walk back to the lorry.

Two minutes later Sandy exited the vehicle. He crawled across the bonnet of the van and fell, exhausted and afraid, to the ground. The van dropped two feet down the bank, and stopped short of the loch, which was a foot deep at that point. There never had been any danger.

The surveyor and foreman felt vindicated. Perhaps Sandy would now concentrate on getting his plotting correct.

Some good came out of the day The survey chain broke when used to pull the van back onto the road. This resulted in the survey for that day being aborted. As a souvenir Sandy took home part of the smashed van manufacturer's plate. His mother went frantic when he explained to her what had happened. He never did tell her about the Loch Ness Monster. After all, he knew it was a myth!

Chapter Sixteen

Soon after leaving The Gazette John commenced work at The Inverness Herald as a junior reporter. John felt that this position had potential for excitement. Not only was he the junior reporter, he was the only reporter. John could see himself acting the part of Clark Kent as Superman, working for The Daily Planet. The only thing missing was Lois Lane.

As the sole reporter he covered sport, court, local government, social and general news. This new work experience was not without its moments and whilst, in the main, most things went right, there was, inevitably, the odd hiccup.

During one of the council meetings in the early part of the year John realised that he had a newsworthy item. The Council had decided that an old, but still used cemetery, was to be turned into a car park, with the remains of the deceased being interred in another cemetery. The scoop, printed on the Thursday, was read with wails of anguish by relatives of those buried in the cemetery. The wails were not entirely of sorrow however, as one concerned protestor revealed, when he made the point that he did not want his mother-in-law dug up, just in case she was still alive.

At the Council meeting the following week John had to apologise to the Council for reporting an incorrect story. The proposal to turn the cemetery into a car park had been turned down. John had his facts all wrong.

Discussed at the same council meeting was concern that the Ferry district was being deprived of certain benefits. John reported the story, but checked the typesetting of the story prior to print. The proposed headline read 'Council state Ferry District depraved'. He tactfully pointed out to the typesetting department that the word should have been 'deprived'.

Privately he completely agreed with the original typesetting.

At a council meeting a few weeks after the cemetery incident the question was debated on whether the streets in the Ferry should be re-named after local councillors. The councillor for the area was Slimey Jefferson, John's old primary school teacher. The proposal to re-name the streets was put to the vote. On a show of hands it became evident that Slimey had fallen asleep, no doubt thinking about tight buttocks.

Slimey awoke, startled, misunderstood what was being said, thinking that it had already been agreed that South Drive would be re-named Jefferson Drive, and promptly fainted. Mr Levitt, fellow councillor, friend, and lodger of Slimey, immediately proceeded to give him the kiss of life, thinking he was suffering from a heart attack. He was dragged off the prostate body by other councillors, to mutterings of "bloody poof."

The Chairman of the Committee, who had arrived at the meeting straight from the Hill Bar, counted the show of hands and declared the vote seven votes to six against the proposal. John was the only person who noticed that there were only twelve councillors at the meeting. The chairman had mistaken the flailing of arms in the fracas as votes against the motion.

The world of reporting was not all failure however. Five months into his reporting job John had a story on the front page of a national newspaper. He had been asked to cover a local athletic meeting. The national press had an interest in the normally insignificant local affair as an attempt was being made on the British one hundred yards sprint record. The newspaper's normal agency reporter was not available.

The record attempt failed, and John duly reported this by telephone to the Glasgow office of the newspaper. He also added the story that a young Frenchman had entered the one mile race, but had stopped after four hundred yards whilst well ahead of the field. John had been sufficiently curious to ask the boy why he had stopped. The French boy could not speak English, but, with John's schoolboy French, and a great deal of sign language, they managed to establish that the boy had entered what he had thought was the four hundred yards race, and had stopped at four hundred yards, believing that he had won the race. This was the story John reported.

John received the princely sum of five guineas from the newspaper for the article. This was more than he earned in two weeks at The Herald.

In the true tradition within his home, where nothing was sacred, one of his sisters opened the letter containing the five guinea cheque. John was the last in the household to know about his windfall.

When the editor of The Herald heard about the scoop he congratulated John, commenting "I always knew you had an eye for news."

John later showed the cheque to his pal Sandy and related how he had earned it.

"But," Sandy pointed out, "you were with me that night at the Ness Islands dance."

"Not for the half-hour you spent chatting up that blonde," John replied. "I took the opportunity to go to the athletic games, got the result, and phoned the newspaper in Glasgow."

"What about the French lad?" Sandy asked.

John looked at Sandy as though Sandy was mad.

"What French lad?" asked John.

"Never let the truth get in the way of a good story. First lesson in reporting," John continued, grinning.

Walter Mitty and Billy Liar were amateurs compared to John.

Following the incident concerning the mis-reporting of the cemetery story, John's editor became more cautious and asserted his authority to edit any stories John submitted. To this end it was agreed that details of all court cases heard would be passed to the editor for approval. John's stories on the court cases usually only covered serious items, such as stealing underwear from a washing line or, more likely, theft from the local Woolworths.

On one particular Thursday the newspaper, at the discretion of the editor, reported that a member of the public had been fined one pound for obstructing the traffic in the town centre. The gentleman in question had taken it upon himself to have a sit-in, on the main road outside the bus depot, in protest at the fact that his bus had been late that morning.

As a consequence he had turned up for work one hour late, sober, but with his first genuine reason in three months for being late, and was promptly dismissed. He decided to consult 'Johnny Walker' who, despite being busy all over town, accommodated the gentleman's need for a discussion.

Following a long talk with his friend Johnny, (by this time he was on Christian name terms), and ably assisted by 'Mr Haig' when Johnny had run out on him after two hours, the drunk (he could no longer be referred to as a gentleman), commenced his sit-in, or to be more precise, lay in. He was so drunk he could not even sit up.

It transpired that the drunk lived in the same street as John's family. John only realised this when he heard the voice of the very irate neighbour berating the lack of loyalty of neighbours after the article had appeared in the newspaper. John had no idea what the neighbour was talking about. He had collected the details of the cases from the Clerk of the Court and had not bothered to read them on the grounds that it was now the editor's responsibility.

The matter was not helped when, two days later, whilst working in the front garden, John saw his father come along the road pushing his bicycle at an angle of forty-five degrees, clearly the worse for wear.

Sods law was at maximum output that day as the wife of the sit-in gentleman was in her front garden at the time. She witnessed the scene. John was convinced that, had there been a telephone handy, the whole of the Highland Constabulary, including the Chief Constable, would have been summoned.

A few weeks after this incident, John thought his luck with women had changed when the same neighbour, smelling of sweet sherry, stated that she would love to get her hands on his body.

"She is older than I would have wished," John reflected," but I have to start somewhere."

His erotic thoughts were later dashed when reeking of after-shave, John leaned over the garden fence to speak to her. In the course of a two minute conversation, mainly from the neighbour, he discovered that the lady worked as an embalmer at a local undertakers. Sex was not what she had on her mind when she said that she wanted to lay her hands on John's body.

Chapter Seventeen

The words 'God Save Our Big Black Queen' could clearly be heard as the National Anthem was played over the tannoy at the Telford Street ground of Inverness Caledonian F.C. Banners waved in the crowd, one of them proudly proclaiming "Stornoway Licensed Victuallers Football Association." Clearly the television reception trials in Stornoway were not yet successful.

The occasion was an international soccer match between South Africa and a Highland League Select. John and Sandy stood in the packed ground. It was 1954 and the lads, both football fanatics, were yelling their support for the Highlanders.

John and Sandy were daft about Caledonian F.C. or 'The Caley' as they were affectionately known. The two other Inverness teams, Clachnacuddin and Thistle, were an irrelevance as far as the boys were concerned.

But that is not to say that the games between the teams were not competed with fierce rivalry.

In 1955 Sandy and John attended a match between Caley and Hamilton Academicals in the Scottish Cup. The spectators huddled for warmth under the corrugated shelter, which masqueraded as an enclosure.

At half-time the fans charged either towards the toilet, (a piece of ground behind a corrugated metal fence), or the stall serving pies and cups of tea. The decision on whether relief or sustenance came first depended on the length of time spent in the public house before the game.

The second-half kicked off, and within thirty seconds the ball was in the Hamilton net. Five seconds later a shower of meat pies rained on the pitch as the inebriated fans rose with their hands in the air, completely forgetting that they were holding their lunch. A further five seconds later and there was bedlam, as the same fans scrambled onto the pitch to retrieve their pies, which by this time were covered in mud.

It took six stewards to regain control when two fans began fighting over the ownership of one of the pies.

Saturday afternoons reached a climax with the checking of football coupons. Households were silenced, as the man of the house huddled over the radio listening to the football results. Not content with getting the results over the radio, he would then rush to the local public house for his copy of the 'The Football Times'.

The husband usually returned several hours later. Frequently without the newspaper, but always with a copy of '*Warcry*'.

Chapter Eighteen

Billy Wilson, the bouncer at the Caley Ballroom, part of the Caledonian Hotel, flexed his muscles. He had seen it all before. There was always one lecher just sitting there ogling the women. It was the fault of management in his opinion. This idea of having tables alongside the dance floor could only lead to trouble. The tables were a perfect viewing point for a nutter. The occupants had no intention of dancing. They just sat there transfixed, watching the girls as they jived. Complaints had been received from some of the male dancers, and the bouncer was under orders to keep an eye on things. No complaints had been received from the female dancers. They appeared to relish the attention.

This particular weirdo was a bit different however. He only looked about fourteen, well under the legal age for admission, and appeared a bit gormless with his thick spectacles and hair soaked with Brylcreem. Billy could not recall the youngster entering the dance hall, but had a vague recollection of having seen him before.

Billy wandered over to the youth. 'Christ' he thought, 'this town is full of nutters'.

It was John's sister's idea that he take up dancing and she encouraged him to attend some of the local dances with her. His depression about not having a girlfriend was affecting the whole family, and this was a hopeful step on the way to resolving the problem. Not that any of the family held much hope of success.

For the older teenagers and adults, dancing was a favourite pastime. One of the dance halls in town was the Northern Meeting Rooms. The Meeting Rooms provided dance facilities on two floors. The ground floor was given over to traditional Scottish country dancing to famous bands such as Jimmy Shand or Bobby McLeod.

The dance tuition at the Kessock was probably the only part of their education that some of the 'Kessie' pupils remembered in later life.

The ground floor was a favourite haunt of squaddies from the local army regiment. A potential suitor was taking his life in his hands if he so much as looked at one of the girls that the squaddies had lined up for the night. This became apparent to John and Sandy when, one Saturday night in August 1956 they attended a dance at The Meeting Rooms. The Clyde Valley Stompers was the attraction on the first floor. During the interval the lads decided to venture to the ground floor. It was here that they ran into the Gordon Highlanders. Not the whole regiment. Just two of them.

It all started quite innocently with John asking one of the girls from his old 'Kessie' school days to dance. The girl in question was Irene Norman, famous for tormenting animals and Willie MacDonald. They were on the floor attempting to dance when they were interrupted by a soldier, the worse for wear, stating that 'John had his bird'.

Irene, seeing that the soldier, despite being drunk, was going to be more entertaining than John, immediately pushed John away from her, into the squaddie, knocking the squaddie to the ground.

The end result was that John and Sandy were chased out of the Meeting Rooms by two of the Gordon Highlanders.

The Caley Ballroom, part of the Caledonian Hotel,

was the favoured spot for those seeking to emulate Fred Astaire or Ginger Rogers. Towards the late fifties this gravitated more towards 'Rock and Roll' and 'The Twist'. But there was still a full programme of Slow Foxtrots, Quicksteps and Waltzes (modern and old-fashioned).

Dances were held on Wednesday nights, with the 'Palais' night on Saturday. All this for four shillings. John would never forget dancing to 'The Tennessee Waltz' played by Harry Shore and His Orchestra.

But whilst the revellers at the Caley and the Meeting Rooms danced to the sounds of Harry Shore or Tubby Hayes, the inebriates in Inverness High Street were dancing The Ferry Tango, to the sounds of 'The Tennants Orchestra' or 'The VP Wine Quintet'.

The Ferry Tango was unique to Inverness. It involved the participation of at least two drunkards holding each other up and swaying, as they tried to find their way home. On special occasions, Hogmanay being the best example, there could be half a dozen or more dancing, each person going in a different direction.

The standard dress for the men attending the Caley dances was always a dark suit with shirt and tie. The girls wore frocks with petticoats and nylon stockings. The teddy-boys, who sported long jackets with velvet collars, drainpipe trousers and brothel creeper shoes, were banned from the Caley, but welcomed at the Meeting Rooms.

Before going out to the Caley, John would preen himself in front of a mirror, singing "A White Sports Coat and a Pink Carnation, I'm all dressed up for the Dance." He had no white coat, or carnation of any colour, but he was always in the mood for a dance.

John was under age to get in to the Caley dance through the main ballroom entrance located at the rear of the hotel. He overcame this by entering the main front lobby of the hotel, and then taking the lift down to the dance area. He then nonchalantly walked into the ballroom area as though he were a hotel resident. He was never challenged when he walked out of the lift straight into the dance foyer.

The Caley had a seating area around the dance floor. For John, this was the most appealing aspect of the dance hall. He would sit there with his drink, watching the girls being swung about the floor, showing acres of nylon stocking top, suspender belt, and, now and then, a glimpse of thigh.

Whilst the lads on the floor were sweating profusely, in an effort to get the girls to twirl round faster, John sat there benefiting from their exertions.

On one such occasion John mistook an enquiry from one of the bouncers who looked at him strangely and asked if he was there to dance. John thanked the bouncer for asking him to dance, but pointed out that he only danced with girls. Five seconds later John was ejected from the Caley. He did not recognise Billy Wilson.

John was so depressed at this turn of events that he briefly contemplated suicide. Then he remembered that there was a Scottish Cup game the following Saturday between Inverness Caley and Forfar Athletic. He decided to defer the suicide until after the match. If Caley won they might just get a good draw in the next round.

Regular Friday and Saturday night dances were held in villages around Inverness. Buses left the Inverness bus depot heading for the village halls of Kirtarlity, Drumnadrochit, Beauly and a dozen other communities where local residents waited, unsure what mayhem would ensue by the end of the evening.

The music in each case was provided by local bands. The halls had a strict 'no alcohol on the premises' policy.

This did not deter the male revellers from imbibing half bottles of whisky, which were discreetly hidden about their person. For the girls a bottle of Babycham or Cherry B was the favoured tipple. It was quite common to find a dance hall with only twenty bodies dancing, whilst the toilets were bursting at the seams with secret drinkers.

The coach would arrive at its destination. Another quick tip of the bottle and into the hall the revellers went – to be confronted by the local lads determined to fight off any approach made on their girls, and by the local women, equally determined to ensure that their husbands or boyfriends did not stray.

After three hours the same crowd of travelling dancers would board the bus and travel back to Inverness, only this time either a bit more friendly or obnoxious, dependent on how the evening had progressed.

It all seemed a bit pointless to John. They may as well have stayed in Inverness all evening and held a dance within the bus terminus buildings.

There were many incidents of over-indulging dancers boarding the wrong bus home. On reaching the end of the journey they would spend hours trying to figure out where they lived, as their hometown had apparently been re-designed during their four hour absence.

The nearest John came to success with the girls at one of the country dances came in the Spring of 1955 when he assisted one of the girls off the bus on its return to Inverness from Kirtarlity. The girl was clearly the worse for wear.

"What's your name and where are you from?" John asked.

"Mary from Elgin," came the barely coherent reply.

John looked at her. There was something vaguely familiar about her. But there was no way she could have travelled all the way from Elgin to a dance at Kiltarlity.

"Let's try again. Where do you live Mary?"

"The Ferry," she replied.

"Right, Mary," John said, "Let's get you home."

Mary put her arm around John, more in need of support than affection, and they proceeded to The Ferry.

They duly arrived at Mary's house. To John's delight he was asked by Mary if he would like to go into the house for a drink, as her mother was not home. John wondered precisely what her mother could be doing at one o'clock in the morning, but he did not particularly care, he had other thoughts on his mind.

He had a touch of déjà-vu on entering the house but had more pressing matters on his mind. It had been a long run from Kiltarlity, and nature was not so much calling, as screaming.

He carefully draped Mary on the settee and looked around for the little room.

The feeling of déjà-vu was getting stronger. The penny dropped when he gazed at himself in the bathroom mirror whilst preening himself to face Mary. He was now getting a feeling of déjà-vu about his earlier déjà-vu.

He drifted back into the living room, in so much of a hurry that he forgot to relieve himself.

"What did you say your name was?" he asked.

"Mary," she replied, "Mary Wilson."

Just then the front door opened and two seconds later John was confronted by an ugly looking woman with henna hair and red finger nails. Recognition was instant. It was Mary Wilson's mother, and it was nail polish, not blood, that he had seen in the window of The Harbour Inn.

As if reading his thoughts Mary spoke.

"Hello Ma," she slurred, "was the Harbour Inn not busy tonight?"

"You!" the henna-haired, blood-fingered harlot shouted, glaring at John. "What the hell are you doing here, and what are you doing with my daughter?"

Mary, who by this time had discarded her top and was lying on the settee, screamed at her mother.

"We've done nothing yet, could you not have come home in half an hour."

"It's not the way it looks," John began to say, when Mary suddenly opened her eyes, stood up, threw her arms around him, and was sick over his suit.

The reaction from the mother was instant. John was literally kicked out of the house in West Drive, the same one he had left eleven years before. The last thing he heard on landing in the pathway outside the house was the voice of moron Mary screaming.

"But he's my boyfriend Ma, I want him back."

John fled.

On the way out of The Ferry he passed Billy Wilson, who had just finished his bouncer duty at The Caley.

The one thing guaranteed about the village hall dances was that you did not know what to expect. You went out there with the innocent intent of finding a girl friend, but anything could happen.

On return from Drumnadrochit on a Friday night in May 1955, John and a dozen other merrymakers were turned off the bus by the police some eight miles from Inverness. It was a bitterly cold and wet night. The police had been on the Drumnadrochit road in order to avoid any confrontation with the drunks in Inverness town centre. Out of sheer boredom they had decided to stop the bus.

On hearing drunken singing from the bus they decided to investigate further. They deemed it unsafe for the bus to proceed when they realised it was overladen. A fellow inebriate, sitting on John's lap, singing "I Belong To

Glasgow," clinched the police decision to off-load some of the revellers.

It was pointed out to the constabulary, by a very drunken and abusive party-goer, that it was a damn sight more dangerous to allow a dozen youngsters to walk eight miles to Inverness in the black of night, than it was to have an overladen bus.

Acting in the true tradition of the Highland Constabulary, who were not known for diplomacy, the police showed sympathy to his point by arresting him for being drunk and disorderly. The drunk got a police car ride to Inverness, the remainder of the dancers walked.

John arrived back in the town centre as a small baker was producing his first batch of bread rolls. He purchased some rolls in order to have a feast when he got home. He arrived home at two o'clock in the morning. His parents were sleeping in the living room. In order to avoid disturbing them he had to enter the house by the back door, en-route to the kitchen.

The back door creaked as John crept into the kitchen towards the light switch. He was immediately assaulted by a blow on the head. Wet fabric clung to his body. He panicked and began to struggle in the dark. The noise awoke his father in the next room.

His father rushed into the kitchen, switched on the light, and there was John draped in wet clothes, sitting on the floor with the clothes pulley around his head.

John was immediately banned from attending any more village dances.

To add insult to injury, when he came down for breakfast several hours later, he discovered that the bread rolls he had purchased in the early hours of the morning, and the sole reason he had entered the house via the kitchen, had been consumed by the family.

Chapter Nineteen

John gazed at the scantily dressed young woman standing in front of him. She was probably about eighteen he thought. His pulse raced and he wondered if he was going to have a heart attack. The girl looked at John and wondered what the goggle-eyed youngster was doing there.

It was the staff changing room at the Playhouse Cinema. John was sixteen at the time, and he had been asked to deliver a message to his sister who was an usherette at the cinema.

Before the half naked girl could ask John who he was the door opened and John's sister entered. She took one look at John's face, and pushed him in the direction of the door. John could not take his eyes off the half naked girl.

He walked straight into the door.

John took a seat in the front stalls and watched the film, but had no idea what the film was about. He was traumatised. He had a feeling in his groin similar to the one that he had when he had visited his friend Sidney in hospital.

The Playhouse was one of three cinemas in Inverness. The Playhouse showed epic films, and boasted a cafeteria which served afternoon teas against a backdrop of fairyland scenes. The scenes were changed every Christmas and were a magical attraction for the children. The Playhouse also had the most attractive usherettes, as John discovered.

The La-Scala Cinema was the children's favourite with its Saturday matinee presentations of cartoons, followed by a main film, usually Old Mother Riley or The Three Stooges. The matinee always ended with the latest episode of the running serial, with the result that the children spent the next seven days wondering if Batman, Flash Gordon, or Tarzan would survive the latest cliffhanger. They had no worries about the western feature films because they always knew that the goodies, (wearing white hats), would beat the baddies (wearing black hats). The La-Scala appealed to those grown-ups who liked the gore, and fear, of the latest horror films.

John's favourite cinema however was the Palace. He lost count of the number of times he played truant in order to see Doris Day musicals. As far as John was concerned, school dinner money was better spent on a one shilling seat in the front stalls, gorging himself on several bars of chocolate, whilst he fantasized about life with Doris.

The only venue for live acts was The Empire Theatre. Sell out crowds attended every performance regardless of who, or what, was appearing. Saturday nights were booked weeks in advance for Andy Stewart, Jimmy Logan or the rare sight of an entertainer from England.

A regular attraction was a hypnotist, who drew enthusiastic guinea pigs onto the stage, to make fools of themselves in front of an open mouthed audience.

Fifty yards down the road, at The Ferry Bar, this scene was acted out every night the pub was open, as the customers, without the benefit of hypnotism, became mesmerised by the demands of Bells and Teachers. The barman had his patrons reacting to his every command.

Other social activities were undertaken. Strolling round the Ness Islands brought out the romantic in John. He often visualised himself with Doris Day, sailing through the Islands to the music of 'Moonlight Bay'.

Open air concerts and dances were held during the summer months in the Ness Islands. The Military Tattoos in the Northern Meeting Park brought large followings of locals and visitors. The Fifty-Fifty Club, a mixed social club for teenagers, was a firm favourite, and an ideal spot for the searching out of other frustrated adolescents. The rampant hormones were kept in check however. The Fifty-Fifty Club was strictly a nice guy, nice girl, tea and biscuits sort of place.

Dances were held at the local Nurses' Home, strictly by invitation only. It was as a result of an invitation to the Nurses' Home that John went 'Up the Hill' for the very first time.

It was probably reasonable to assume that a nurse, attending a dance in a Nurses' Home, actually lived in the Home. John was to find that this logic held no water, when a young nurse asked him to walk her home.

As the front door to the nurses' living quarters was about twenty yards from the function room, John was about to decline the request, when the girl added, "I don't live in the Home, of course, I live about a mile away."

With this announcement John's heart leapt.

The trainee nurse continued, "I live up the Hill with my grandmother. My name is Alison, Alison Forbes."

John thought, 'What a strange name, Alison, Alison'. Still, she lived 'Up The Hill', and fancy names were normal up there.

John's heart started beating faster. Whether it was in anticipation at the proximity of a female, or the thought of visiting the Hill district for the first time, he was not sure. With legs trembling he started the journey. The fact his legs were trembling was rather unfortunate, as the first obstacle he had to face was a swing-bridge across the

River Ness, leading to the Hill district.

The bridge shook violently as John, terrified, clutched the nurse closer to him. She took this as a sign of amour and pulled him closer to her.

"My, you are a fast worker aren't you?" she said.

John was so intent on trying to remember the route which would take him back out of the Hill District, that he failed to notice the surveillance policeman, Probationary Police Constable David Thompson, pushing his unlit bicycle, twenty yards behind John and Alison. The policeman kept his distance. He knew a Ferry or Dalneigh toe-rag when he saw one. He wondered what no good the toe-rag was up to heading for the Hill district. More importantly, he recognised the little sod from some time in the past. He also recognised the girl. P.P.C. Thompson had a memory for faces. One day he would remember where he had seen them both before.

Twenty minutes later, having passed houses bigger than he had ever seen in his life, John arrived at Hill House. By this time Alison was demonstrating the kiss of life.

On entering the house Alison removed John's jacket and offered him tea and biscuits, at the same time putting a photograph album of family snaps in front of him. John would have preferred something stronger than tea but did not want to spoil the occasion, or blur his memory for his escape route from the Hill District. He remembered the warning his father had given him.

"I'm so glad I met you," she began, "I knew as soon as I saw you at the dance that we were of a kindred spirit. You are so different from those Council estate lads. How any sensible girl would be seen with anybody from the Ferry or Dalneigh is beyond me."

She opened the photograph album. There was one of

her in a bikini sitting on a beach in a sun filled location.

"This is me in Tenerife," said Alison. "Do you ever go overseas?"

John thought quickly.

"Yes," he replied, thinking of the Eilean Dubh and the Black Isle. "My family and I have been overseas a few times."

A few minutes later John advised Alison that he had been Dux at Aberdeen Academy, and was now at University. John found that his accent had changed in a matter of minutes. He had felt for some time that he was too good to be living in the Ferry or Dalneigh. Even his friends had commented on how different he was, although they used the word 'odd' rather than 'different'.

A picture of two women caught his eye.

"Who are they?" he enquired, trying to sound as interested as he could.

"That's my grandmother and my mother," replied Alison. "My grandmother was a midwife about seventeen years ago, but she had a nervous breakdown. The family never did find out why, but it appears that she had some trouble with the police. Poor soul, all she does now is sit in her room playing with a bicycle torch. My father died just before I was born. My mother met him whilst she was working for the Government during the war. My mother never married, but she explained to me that my father was a top official in the Food Ministry, a Mr Jonathan Winngate. My mother died five years ago. I have no other relatives."

John thought back to stories he had heard about his earlier life in the Ferry, and the stories of the three midwives who had required medical counselling. He vaguely recalled something about a bicycle type known as a Raleigh F.S. He also recalled stories of Jocky Winngate and his illegitimate brats.

John felt that he needed some breathing space. Was there possibly some connection between Jocky and Alison. Surely not! She was the epitome of good taste, whereas Jocky was, well 'Jocky'. There was no other word to describe him.

"Good heavens, is that the time?" John exclaimed, standing up. "I've just remembered that I have an important exam tomorrow, must rush if I am to achieve my ambition of being a brain surgeon."

But John was smitten. This was the type of girl he had always wanted. But he had been smitten before. In fact if 'smitten' had been an illness, John would have been critically ill.

John was twenty yards out of the house when he was stopped by P.P.C. Thompson and interrogated. The policeman had obviously seen too many 'B' thrillers at the La-Scala. He shone a torch in John's face whilst demanding a confession. Any confession would do.

John gave his name as Sandy Roberts.

John vowed he would see Alison again.

But he also vowed never to visit The Hill district again unless he was with a reliable witness.

Regular funfairs and circuses were held in a field near the Ness Islands. Whilst these were entertaining in their own right, the biggest thrill of the evening for John, Sandy and their mates was taking the short cut home through the adjacent cemetery, each one of them terrified, but trying to save face.

There were very few occasions that they managed to take the whole walk at a leisurely stroll. The last hundred yards was inevitably a fast sprint, before clambering over the cemetery railings at the risk of injury, or at the very least, torn trousers.

The fast sprint, however, was not without some

justification. On a memorable evening in the summer of 1955, with the light just fading and the sound of a funfair receding in the distance, two adventurous souls climbed over the railings, and began a casual walk on their short cut home. The casual walk suddenly turned into panic as, out of the corner of his eye, John discerned a white figure arising from one of the gravestones. Screaming like banshees the boys fled the cemetery, not noticing two pale figures disappearing in the opposite direction.

The screams quickly brought a call to the police. Within minutes the police had arrived at the cemetery. It was the caller's mention of the word 'naked' that prompted the speedy response. Had there just been screams the constabulary would have headed towards Drumnadrochit, well away from any possible trouble.

John was attending the Sheriff Court two days later, in his reporting role, when an unusual case was heard. It appeared that a call to the police two evenings earlier had resulted in the arrest of a man and a woman, both naked, the male on the street side of the cemetery railings, and the female within the cemetery. She was trying to climb over the railings, but because of her size was unable to do so.

It transpired that the couple had attended a funeral in the cemetery late that afternoon, had drunk a half bottle of Scotch, and had found themselves locked in the cemetery.

The sheriff dropped the case when it was revealed that the corpse at the funeral had been the woman's husband, and her lover was the brother of the deceased. The woman was referred for treatment.

Burns Nights were held in most of the social clubs and John was greatly surprised when he was asked, at the age of seventeen, to propose the traditional 'Toast to the Lassies' at the local church Burns Supper. This duty involved saying a few words in honour of the lassies, followed by a toast in whisky.

Considering his success with girls to date, the 'Kessie', the 'High', the Caley Ballroom and America all came to mind, this could have been an excellent opportunity for John to tell the world what he really thought of the short-sightedness of both local, and international, females. Had he been given the traditional whisky he may well have done. Because of his age, and the fact it was a church activity, he was provided with a glass of raspberry cordial.

John spoke glowingly about 'the Lassies'. His comments were directed at Moira, the vicar's daughter, now a sylphlike figure, sitting opposite him. He had seen no sign of her executing her declared intention of becoming a nun. Every opportunity had to be seized.

By his late-teens John had become an avid reader. He found pleasure in reading his older brother's Hank Jansen novels, True Detective Magazines and Hornblower epics, all without his brother's knowledge.

His greatest reading pleasure however, was his brother's well thumbed copy of Health and Efficiency – a nudist magazine, which was kept hidden under his brother's mattress.

Chapter Twenty

Hogmanay in Scotland is always of special significance. New Years Eve 1955 was even more significant for John, as it was the first New Year that he was treated as an adult. He was allowed to go out on his own, to take in the New Year and go first footing.

At midnight he stood outside the Town Hall along with hundreds of other revellers, waiting for the clock to strike, and the bells to ring. He returned home at one in the morning, having briefly first-footed some friends on the way, to find a party in full swing. Several of his neighbours and relatives were there. His parents joined in the singing of many favourite Scottish songs as a Ceilidh got under way. The singing of 'Grannies Heilan Hame', and 'Maggie', had always been of special significance to John's parents.

This was John's first grown-up New Year's Eve with his parents.

He had no idea that it was to be the last with his mother.

On a cold morning, in September 1956, John was working in The Herald newspaper office when he received a telephone call stressing that he should come home straight away. He walked home, full of sadness, not sure what to expect, but expecting the worst.

On arrival at his home he could see that all the curtains were drawn – a sign of death in the house.

His mother had been ill for some time. In the last few

weeks of her illness none of the sons of the house had been allowed to see her. His mother had been attended daily by John's father and his sisters.

The day before his mother's funeral, John was allowed to see her to say his last good-bye. He kissed her cheek, and hoped that he had been a good son to her. The following morning he stood at the foot of the stairs, as her coffin was carried out of the house by the funeral directors. He did not want her to go.

The funeral cortege left the house on the short journey to the cemetery. The whole neighbourhood followed the hearse, with John's father and the children leading the mourners.

The house was full of sobbing for several months.

In the same week that John's mother died, his friend Sidney Brown, the lad with rheumatic fever, died of heart failure.

John was beginning to realise that life could be cruel.

His world of childhood security had changed forever.

Chapter Twenty-One

The fifties was a particularly good time for meaningful music. Songs had lyrics that could be listened to and be carried away by. One song in particular had a great effect on John. 'You Belong To Me' with the invitation to 'see the Pyramids along the Nile, watch the sun set on a tropic isle'.

The death of his mother was the catalyst in John reaching a decision.

In December 1956, three months after the death of his mother, John advised his father that he was leaving home to join the Royal Air Force. His father gave John his blessing. Although John realised that leaving was unfair on his father who was still suffering a great loss, he felt that he had to get away.

John's decision to join the Air Force was not a sign that he was maturing or feeling brave. On the contrary. National Service was imminent and in view of his earlier Army Cadet experience the Army was out of the question. He toyed with the idea of joining the Royal Navy, but then remembered his experiences going on picnics to the Black Isle on the ferryboat, Eilean Dubh.

A chapter in John's life had come to an end. He no longer believed in vampires, fairies, or Father Christmas. He had progressed from infancy to adolescence, a period full of childhood and teenage memories.

His lack of finesse with the girls was beginning to affect him. However, by the age of seventeen he had only experienced the delights of Mary from the Ferry and

Alison from up the Hill. He had never had a proper girlfriend although he was still hopeful about Alison. Provided of course that she never found out about his background.

With a deep sigh, he packed his few possessions.

He was stepping from a world of childhood into uncharted waters.

But John had two things in his favour.

His vivid imagination and his survival skills from the Ferry.

In March 1957 John left Inverness.

Chapter Twenty-Two

ENGLAND, MARCH 1957

The tear gas was making John's eyes water and his breathing difficult. He could hear voices screaming at him to get out of the way. He received a violent shove from behind and he stumbled, gasping for breath, out of the shelter and into the fresh air. A figure stood in front of him.

"You stupid sod, Urquhart," a voice stated. "Are you trying to get us all killed?"

John was at R.A.F. West Kirby, six weeks into his square bashing, and had just completed the drill for coping with a tear gas incident.

The Drill Sergeant looked down at him with contempt, and growled, "You, Urquhart, are a strong candidate for back flighting."

Eight weeks earlier John had reported to the R.A.F. recruitment office in Inverness to be informed that, subject to a medical, he was to be accepted for R.A.F. service. His medical was held at an Air Force base close to Inverness. Because of his bad eyesight he was eliminated from any aircrew activity. Options offered were in the trades of Court Shorthand Writer, serving at military courts martial, and Russian Translator. He found the idea of Russia exciting, but was advised that, in order to be trained for this, he had to sign on for five years.

He declined both options, on the grounds that his main reason for joining the R.A.F. was to get out of doing two years National Service in an Army regiment. He was prepared to do three years service in the R.A.F. but five years was out of the question.

By this time it was evident to the recruiting staff that John was looking for a good time.

Accordingly he was recruited into the trade of Air Movements. This was exactly what John wanted. It meant working on aircraft, and the nature of the work virtually guaranteed an overseas posting.

The week following his medical he reported to R.A.F. Cardington, in the south of England. He was about to meet the English on their own territory.

At Cardington he was issued with his formal Identity Card, Form 1250. This form, along with Form 252 (used for processing disciplinary offences), were to be his close companion for the next three years.

Kit was issued comprising a variety of clothing items, including two uniforms, a greatcoat, drawers cellular (five pairs), a housewife (sewing kit), shoe brushes, and a metal appliance designed to keep blanco off his 'best blue' uniform whilst polishing the buttons. John had never owned so much.

On receipt of the uniforms and greatcoat John checked for previous nametags. He did not want a repeat of the Billy Wilson incident. But all the kit was new. Not only was it new, it was his. For the first time in his life he had three different sets of clothes to wear. John took great care in marking all of his kit with his name and service number.

He proceeded from Cardington to West Kirby, near Liverpool, for eight weeks square bashing. He was billeted with nineteen other youths, most of them away from home for the first time. He heard accents from all over the United Kingdom.

There was a great feeling of esprit de corps with the recruits. The shared view was that they were all facing the same difficulties. This had the effect of pulling them together, and allowed for the making of many friendships over the following weeks.

Square bashing was a total contrast to John's serene life in Inverness. Weeks were spent on drilling, bayonet practice, rifle practice, unarmed combat, riot drill and loads of bull – the art of cleaning and polishing when not needed.

He became an expert at cleaning toilets and bumpering floors. From being a seven stone weakling he was developing into a seven stone wreck.

The recruits marched everywhere at the double, and lined up in crocodile fashion. Just like the Kessock School. They clutched their eating irons and metal drinking mugs behind their backs, waiting to be served with the delicacies of the day. In most cases this consisted of powdered eggs or powdered potatoes, with meat and vegetables produced from large tins. But there was no shortage of food.

'Lights out' was at ten-thirty in the evening, with reveille seeming to arrive moments later at six a.m. By the end of the third week some of the recruits had been reduced to tears. Rumours abounded about recruits on earlier courses who had committed suicide rather than complete the course.

But there were bright moments. The mid morning and afternoon tea breaks in the N.A.A.F.I., when they sat down for a well earned fifteen minute rest, listening to juke box favourites. And the hour in the evening, prior to lights out, when they reminisced about home and loved ones.

At the end of the fourth week of training the recruits were allowed a weekend break to visit their families. John decided to go home to Inverness and wear his new Best

Blue uniform to the Caley dance.

En-route to Inverness he changed trains in Glasgow. This allowed him an hour to explore Glasgow.

He entered a public house just outside the railway station. He was still only seventeen.

He was immediately confronted by two Gordon Highlanders. John heard the words "R.A.F. English ponce."

He pointed out that he was not English. This still left the ponce bit in the air.

Recognition dawned on both parties at the same time.

"It's that little sod from the Meeting Rooms in Inverness. The one who got us banned," a broad Scots accent exclaimed.

John fled, pursued by The Gordons. But John had plenty of practice at this exercise, and he eluded them.

The seven stone weakling had returned.

At the dance John wore his old grey work-suit. The one his father had bought him when he started work. The suit was showing signs of wear by this stage, but at long last it fitted him.

On the fifth week of training a weekend was spent roughing it in the Welsh mountains. Tents were assembled using waterproof groundsheets. This meant sleeping on the ground. The recruits had no bedding. They had to rely on close body contact to keep warm. John knew all about this from his bed sharing experience as a child.

Having related to his fellow recruits about his experiences with The Boys Brigade, and his skills on erecting tents, John was elected to oversee the setting up of the camp. The experiences of his youth camping days however were a million miles away from the barrenness and freezing cold of the Welsh hills.

Washing and shaving was undertaken using icy spring

water which cascaded down the hillside, frequently through the tents. The instructors had cynically allowed the recruits to pitch their tents where the recruits thought to be the most suitable spot. Needless to say the recruits, led by John, picked the wrong spot.

The nights were the longest, coldest, wettest, and most miserable that could possibly be experienced. A homosexual masochist would have loved it. John hated Wales with a passion.

But life had its compensations. Two days after arriving at the Welsh site the recruits boarded the transport to take them back to West Kirby. They left the mountains at five o' clock in the morning. At eight o'clock they stopped at a roadside café for breakfast.

They were only in the café ten minutes when the corporal instructor ordered them to get on their feet and board the truck. Some of them had not even received their food order.

The recruits stood reluctantly, muttering under their breath as they did so.

This should have been the moment for the corporal to acknowledge that the recruits required more time.

The words Military Intelligence proved to be an oxymoron.

The corporal had already earmarked John as a probable ringleader in any dissent. He looked at John straight away.

"Did you say something, Urquhart?" the corporal snarled.

Before John had a chance to reply a wet tea cloth had wrapped itself around the head of the corporal, and an irate buxom café owner had pushed the corporal violently out the door.

"Out!" she screamed, seeing the possibility of her best

trade for weeks disappearing. "Leave my customers alone."

The corporal fell on the ground outside the café, picked himself up, and tried to re-enter, only to find the door slammed in his face.

"Right, you lot," said the well-endowed proprietress. "Finish your tea in peace." She turned the key in the lock as she spoke. The café was in uproar. Cheering airmen gazed at the woman in awe, and the more foolhardy, John included, looked out of the window at the corporal, who by this time had been joined by the sergeant.

Fifteen minutes later the recruits were released from the café. The café proprietress approached John and, thrusting her ample bosom into his face, stated, "You don't have to pay son. Don't worry, I'll look after you."

Her eyes were swimming with emotion as she furtively handed John a piece of paper.

John looked at the paper. "My telephone number," the fifty year old woman stated, "Just in case you come back this way."

Two minutes later John was on a charge of incitement to riot.

On return to camp he was interrogated by the sergeant prior to meeting the Flight Commander for his punishment. The concept of innocence before guilt was not part of military culture. John suggested to the sergeant that he be allowed to call the café owner as his witness. The sergeant considered for a few seconds, remembering the size of the woman.

The matter was dropped.

But John's cards were marked.

Several days after this incident the recruits were asked if any of them had special skills. John mentioned his knowledge of shorthand, thinking that this could mean a good skive in Station Headquarters, away from the parade ground. Not so. The drill corporal seized on this news with glee, declaring, "Shorthand, excellent, report to the guard-room. They are short-handed for guard duties."

John had learned the golden rule of the armed forces. "Never volunteer."

Back-flighting was a constant threat for the recruits. The threat would be made if a recruit was failing to reach a laid down standard. This would result in a recruit being given an additional two weeks training. This was a major concern to young recruits already close to breaking point. John was deeply concerned. He had already been earmarked as a candidate because of the café and the tear gas incidents.

The passing out parade rehearsal allowed John another opportunity to blot his copybook. The recruits were on the final part of the rehearsal with a 'present arms' salute. The band was there for rehearsal. The four squadrons of recruits were drawn up on the parade ground, trousers pressed, buttons gleaming, and eyes sparkling, at the thought that, in a few days time, they would be home on leave.

John was one step ahead of them.

His mind was in the Caley Ballroom in Inverness, poncing about in his 'best blue' uniform, impressing Alison. He had forgotten about the Glasgow Gordon Highlanders incident by this time.

The command came. "Present arms."

Seven hundred and ninety-nine bodies presented arms.

John stood there, an inane grin on his face.

He was in the middle of a slow foxtrot, and was about to make his pitch to Alison, when his concentration was interrupted. He had actually moved forward two steps, holding his rifle close to him in the belief that it was

Alison, when a voice bellowed in his ear.

"For Christ's sake, Urquhart, what the hell are you doing?" the voice roared.

John awoke, dropped his rifle, and found himself staring at the face of the café corporal, who had a manic grin on his face.

"Get back to the billet now and pack your kit," the corporal thundered. "You're back-flighted."

John fled the parade ground listening to the silence. Nobody dared snigger or titter. Back-flighting was a serious subject. He entered the billet. It was immaculate. All the beds had kit laid out for inspection by the Flight Commander. He was heartbroken. He could not entertain the thought of a further two weeks square-bashing. Desertion crossed his mind.

He despairingly began to pack his kit into his duffel bags ready for his move, and had just completed the task, when his room-mates piled into the room in preparation for the kit inspection. There were condolences all round.

Five minutes later the corporal entered the room and glanced round. He looked at John's bed, his face fell, and he asked, "Where's all your kit?"

"Here, corporal," John replied, pointing to his duffle bag.

The corporal looked at John in dismay.

"Eight weeks you've been here, Urquhart, and this is the first bloody time you've carried out an order as instructed. Why pick now?"

The corporal grabbed John by the arm and dragged him along the floor. John's kit bag was caught around his ankles and he had great difficulty in keeping pace. They stopped at the latrines just outside the billet.

"Stay there until I tell you to come out," the corporal thundered, as he pushed John into the toilets.

As the corporal closed the door, John saw the figures of the Drill Sergeant and Flight Commander enter the billet. One hour later he was released from the latrines by his room mates. The corporal had completely forgotten all about him. John was not back-flighted.

At the end of eight weeks square bashing he was posted to R.A.F. Northolt, in South London, to learn his trade of Air Movements.

He never ever wanted to see a place like West Kirby again.

.

Chapter Twenty-Three

802 A.C.2 Urquhart.
Hut 314,
Trenchard Squadron,
R.A.F. West Kirby.
Nr. Liverpool
England

1 May 1957

Mr J. Urquhart.
343 Laurel Avenue,
Inverness

Dear Dad,

I received your letter. Sorry to hear about granddad's horse dying. Still he was quite old. I assume he will have been disposed of in the normal way and turned into glue and compost. It is a disgraceful way to be treated after such a hard working life.

Square bashing has been great fun and a piece of cake. All the other lads have benefited a great deal from my camping experiences. We recently had a weekend in the Welsh mountains. It was wonderful. Wales is almost as beautiful as Scotland. I must go back there for a visit one day.

The drill instructors are all friendly and I get on extremely well with them. I suspect that my previous army cadet experience helps. I fall into discipline quite naturally. I must have picked up this flair from your experiences in Burma. We hold our passing out parade in a couple of days. I should be in the running for 'Top Recruit' as I stood out at the rehearsal. I was singled out by the drill instructor who advised me that he had never come across any recruit quite like me before.

I visited Liverpool on Saturday and saw 'The Platters' in concert. After the show I visited Lime Street with my mates. At one stage I lost them. The area was frequented by some very strange women. A policeman asked me what I was doing in the area. When I said I was looking for a friend he asked me to leave before I got arrested. There must have been a security alert in the area.

Tell brother James that I am sorry that I ruined his Health and Efficiency magazine by putting it back under his mattress wet. It was silly of me to read it in the bath. I have been to a shop in Lime Street who advise me that they have a better magazine, and are sending this direct to James. I have paid for this so I am sure he will be pleased.

Well Dad I must close now as the drill corporal is waving to me. I expect he wants to thank me.

Give my love to the rest of the family.

Your loving son,

John Urquhart 802 A.C.2

Chapter Twenty-Four

802 AC2 Urquhart
Hut 16,
R.A.F. Kidbrooke,
London S.E.12

28 May 1957

Mr J. Urquhart,
343 Laurel Avenue,
Inverness.

Dear Dad,

I received your letter and although I can understand how upset you are I should explain that I mis-read your earlier letter. I thought you had said that granddad's horse had died.

I am sorry to hear about granddad's death. My earlier comments about glue and compost should be ignored.

I am at a loss to understand why James's book went to Mr Wallace, our next door neighbour. It is hardly my fault that Norma, his daughter, opened the plain brown envelope, and has been treated for shock since then. I suppose at thirteen she is a bit young to be looking at such things. The book shop in Liverpool told me that the replacement book would be similar to Health and Efficiency, not the type of book sent. I had never heard of

Strumpet until now. When the Highland Constabulary get in touch with me I shall explain what happened.

I did not get the Top Recruit at square bashing, but I am heading for better things on my Air Movements course. I go for my first flight next week. I am told that the Beverley Aircraft is a giant of a machine. I am quite excited at the thought.

If you let me have the ward number where Norma is I shall send her a card. I shall pick it myself this time. Ha Ha. That was a joke.

Your loving son,

John Urquhart A.C.2 (soon to be A.C.1)

Chapter Twenty-Five

The 40,000 crowd at Highbury, home of Arsenal F.C. were holding their breath. Arsenal were playing Chelsea in a key league fixture. The big centre forward strode forward and thumped the ball into the top left hand corner of the net. The Arsenal fans, John included, went mad.

It was John's first visit to a major football ground. The English First Division, and here he was, the Lad from The Ferry, watching two of England's top teams in action. He could not believe his luck. Only nine weeks before he had been watching Caley reserves play against Lossiemouth reserves in front of fifty-six spectators. This included the chap who served the teas and pies.

John was at R.A.F. Kidbrooke on his Air Movements training course. Kidbrooke was a contrast to West Kirby. There was still an element of discipline but not with the intensity there had been at square-bashing. John quickly settled into a comfortable routine. It was all classroom work, mainly mathematics, calculating the trim of aircraft. He quickly became familiar with the terms fuel payload, prioritisation, AOG spares and other expressions peculiar to the R.A.F.

It was not aircrew. But this was the world John had been craving for.

Accommodation for the trainees was similar to West Kirby, with twenty to a billet. There was no drill, apart from the crocodile walks from classroom to classroom, no rifle range, no gas shelters and, best of all, no stroppy drill instructors.

Kidbrooke was close to the core of London and John seized every opportunity to explore. He visited the London theatres, using free tickets provided to servicemen. He stayed in the centre of London at the Union Jack Club, a hotel for servicemen. He felt that he was living at last.

John took the opportunity to visit Petticoat Lane, the Mecca of street vending. Accompanied by several of his mates he travelled from Kidbrooke on a Sunday morning. He was not disappointed. There were stalls everywhere. The Inverness market paled into insignificance.

He was conned of course. But that was part of the learning curve of Petticoat Lane. He purchased a Parker pen and a bottle of Chanel perfume. The pen leaked and the perfume smelled like vinegar. John knew the smell of vinegar. He even knew the taste.

John could see that there were opportunities for an exchange of knowledge between the London traders and the kids from the Ferry. He had not seen Marie Winngate for many years, but he knew that, even at seven years of age, Marie could have taught Petticoat Lane a thing or two.

In the final week of the course John took his first flight in an aircraft. It was the most frightening experience of his life.

The Air Movements Clerk at R.A.F. Abingdon handed John a paper bag as John was about to board the aircraft. John enquired what it was for. The mover replied, "It's your sick-bag."

The thirty potential movers trooped onto the aircraft. It was not quite what they were expecting.

"Where are the seats?" queried several voices in unison.

The Air Quartermaster pointed to webbing straps fixed to the side of the aircraft.

"There," he replied, "now strap yourself in."

There was a moment of panic when one of the more knowledgeable trainees passed the comment that the webbing seats were the type used by parachutists prior to jumping from an aircraft. Wails of anguish greeted this news. The Quartermaster quickly pacified them. He re-assured them that they were not expected to execute a parachute jump. "Unless, of course, we run into problems," he concluded.

"Don't forget to check that your life-jacket is attached to your webbing," the Quartermaster continued. "Your parachutes are stacked in the middle of the floor."

By now thirty reluctant airmen were strapping themselves securely into their seats. The excitement at the thought of their first flight had been replaced by fear.

The Beverley engines roared, and the aircraft prepared for take-off.

It was John who noticed that the rear doors of the aircraft were wide open.

"Sergeant!" he yelled at the Quartermaster, above the roar of the engines. "The door is not closed."

"How the hell do you expect to get the freight out of the aircraft if the door is closed?" replied the Quartermaster. "We are doing circuits and bumps over the Wiltshire downs, and are also practising our freight despatch drill."

Forty minutes later the trainees, who by now had wished they had never left home, trooped off the aircraft. Each one carried a full sick-bag. The aircraft had touched down and taken off six times during the forty minutes. The Quartermaster had sought the help of each of them as he unchained freight which was tied down in the centre of the aircraft. Once the freight was free of its fastenings, a webbing strap, attached to the inside of the aircraft, was the only thing holding the recruits back as they each took it in turns to assist the Quartermaster by pushing the freight along rollers, until it disappeared out the back of the aircraft into oblivion.

After landing, a de-briefing was held. It was explained to John and his colleagues that the Beverley flight was a one-off and that it was most unlikely they would ever go through the experience again.

By this time John could not care less. He was seriously contemplating a transfer to the Black Watch Regiment. Anything was better than working with aircraft.

At the end of the course John received an A1 pass. He was now an Aircraftsman First Class. He was posted to R.A.F. Lyneham, home station to squadrons of Comets, Hastings and Britannia aircraft.

Chapter Twenty-Six

On arrival at R.A.F. Lyneham John found himself sharing a billet with twenty other airmen. After three months in the Royal Air Force he found himself thinking fondly of the times when he shared a room with only two other people.

The early months of winter were setting in, and the cold wind blasting across the airfield brought misery to the hut occupants. The coke fires in the huts were constantly emitting noxious fumes. It was a choice between freezing or poisoning.

The work at Lyneham was hard for John. At training he had only seen the classroom aspect of the trade. As a newcomer to the trade he was detailed for duties involving the loading and unloading of aircraft. He was not allowed near a trim-sheet. He was not allowed to calculate how much fuel it took to get from Lyneham to Cyprus, how much payload capacity required for passengers and freight, the safety equipment required, and the sequence of loading. Instead he was a humper and a mover.

He loaded aircraft in mid-morning and in the middle of the night. A crisis would arrive necessitating flights to destinations John had never heard of. The movers would be turfed out of bed. Bedding, food, and medical supplies to Africa. Ammunition and desert clothing to British Army units in the Middle East. The commodity could be anything. The destination anywhere in the world. It was all a new experience for John, at times frightening, at times bewildering.

John was accident prone. He was also careless. A deadly combination. If John could avoid doing something, he would avoid it.

This resulted in a couple of incidents, humorous in retrospect, potentially dangerous at the time.

Both incidents occurred within the same week. John had been detailed to check the seating configuration on two aircraft. It was the middle of the night, winter, and he did not feel like hanging about.

He arrived at the aircraft.

Problem! No lights on the aircraft.

Not a problem if he followed procedures.

But it was cold, and John could not be bothered to connect the trolley-ack to the aircraft in order to obtain lighting. Instead he entered the darkness of the aircraft and slowly began to walk along the aisle, his hand on the back of each seat as he counted the number of seats fitted.

He was in the middle of the Comet when he fell through an open hatch in the floor. The engineers, when checking the electrical functions of the aircraft, had left the electrical hatch open.

He only fell a couple of feet. His body was jammed between the seats and the open hatch. He suffered superficial injuries.

Never one to learn from his mistakes, four days later John had his second mishap. He walked out of an aircraft and fell straight to the ground. There were two things in his favour. The aircraft was on the ground at the time, and it was a Hastings. The door was only a few feet off the tarmac.

It transpired that an over-zealous mover, clearly as conscientious as John, had taken the steps away from the aircraft without first checking that the aircraft was empty. Once again the injuries were superficial.

The months at Lyneham sped by. The highlight of the working day was the visit of the Salvation Army wagon with its tea and rolls, for the morning breaks of the airmen working on the runway. John felt quite nostalgic standing outside the Sally Ann van. He felt as though he was an old and valued customer. He was not sure if he should thank the ladies in the van for the clothing they had sent him as a child.

Christmas 1957 was the first time that John had spent his combined Christmas Day birthday away from home.

It was a memorable one.

He spent Christmas Day in the guard room cells.

It was the Scrumpy that did it.

Christmas Eve saw John in a pub located close to the camp. The evening started quietly enough with John, and another Scots lad from Dundee, sipping their cider. They both felt the cider was preferable to the English beer.

An hour into the evening John, and the Dundee fruitcake, having by now finished two pints of the lethal Scrumpy, were singing songs from the homeland. They were joined in a rendition of 'The Northern Lights of Old Aberdeen' and 'I Belong to Glasgow' by a seventy-five year old woman who was visiting the pub for a quiet Christmas Eve drink with her R.A.F. officer son-in-law.

John should have known better. The last time he had sung 'I Belong to Glasgow' was when he had been turned off the bus after the Kiltarlity dance. He thought of Mary Wilson. It could have been that the seveny-five year old woman reminded him of Mary's mother.

He had a recollection of dancing a Highland Fling with the woman, and telling her son in law to 'sod-off'. The elderly woman took John's side in the discussion, hitting her son-in-law with her walking stick. The landlord called the police.

The R.A.F. police decided to defer any charges until after the New Year. They were not to know that, by doing this, they would save themselves some time.

New Year's Eve saw John at a dance in Swindon. He had learned his lesson about drinking Scrumpy and opted instead for cans of lager.

The particular brew he favoured was Tennants lager. As a marketing ploy the cans had pictures of girls on the side. John decided to go for the full collection of eight pictures. After the eighth can he had two cans with a picture of Christine and one each of Caroline, Rosalyn, Karen, Elizabeth, Denise and Moira.

Having missed out on his complete set of German aircraft by one card. John was determined to be successful this time. He asked for a further can of lager.

The very attractive barmaid looked at John and asked, with concern in her voice, "Are you OK?"

John looked at the barmaid and, in a slurred voice, with a pronounced broad Scottish accent, no doubt influenced by the Scottish lager, replied, "No, I'm looking for Alison."

"Did she come in with you?" the girl asked.

John looked at the barmaid.

"Who?" he asked.

The barmaid, seeing that she was not going to get any sense out of John, suggested that he have a coffee.

John completely misunderstood the suggestion and took the girl to mean 'Why don't you come home for a coffee?'

He sat in the bar for the next hour, nursing his empty cans of lager, pining for Alison, the girl on the missing can, and his girl in Inverness. His eyes flitted from one can to the other, trying to determine which one was the most attractive.

After his Christmas Eve episode, involving the seventy-five year old Scrumpy woman, he found them all attractive.

Eleven o'clock brought closing time and John went outside to wait for the barmaid. He could hear calls of "Have A Good New Year" echoing as patrons left the pub.

The barmaid walked out of the pub, and was confronted by John.

"Yes" she asked nervously.

"I'm waiting for my coffee" John replied, clutching the empty cans to his breast. He had discarded the surplus Christine.

Not for the first time in his life a girl ran away from John screaming.

John fled down the road. 'Christ' he thought as he ran, 'this is getting to be a habit'.

He was picked up by the police one mile outside Swindon and was taken back to R.A.F. Lyneham for another night in the cells.

In the first week in January 1958 John was sentenced to thirty days confinement to camp. In the second week of January he received notification that he was being posted to R.A.F. El Adem, in the Libyan Desert for two years.

John's confinement to camp was temporarily suspended in order that he could proceed on one weeks embarkation leave.

On John's embarkation leave in Inverness he and Sandy attended a dance at the Nurses' Home. John saw Alison there. The attraction was still mutual. Although she had to point out that her name was Alison, not Alison Alison.

John was denied the opportunity to take Alison to her home in the Hill district. Her grandmother had been hospitalised and Alison had moved into the Nurses' Home on a temporary basis during the hospitalisation period.

John promised Alison that he would write to her as soon as he arrived at the Officers Mess at his new station. He could not give any more details, as he was on a secret mission.

John was just leaving the Nurses' Home when he noticed a stunning girl talking to a young man. She looked vaguely familiar and, catching John's eye, she smiled at him. At that moment Sandy dragged John out of the home. There was still time to catch the last dance at the Caley. There was still a chance to score.

The night before flying out to Libya, John was on duty in the Movements Section at Lyneham. It was three o'clock in the morning. There was, for a change, no aircraft to be worked on. It was too cold to sleep in the hangar. John wandered through the freight despatch area.

The fork-lift was sitting there, waiting to create havoc. John sat in the driving seat. He had never driven anything before, apart from a pedal car. He turned the engine on, and pressed his foot on a lever. The forklift shot forward, straight through a crate bearing the label 'AOG spares. Fragile. For immediate despatch'.

John knew what AOG meant. 'Aircraft on Ground'.

An R.A.F. aircraft was sitting on the ground, somewhere in the world, awaiting the spares, before it could become operational again.

John turned off the forklift and left it where it had stopped, with one fork through the spares. He walked out of the hangar in an effort to find something to do that was less hazardous.

Later that morning John reported to Stanstead Airport for his flight to Libya. The overseas travel he had hoped for had begun.

Meanwhile, back in Inverness, there was turmoil in the Urquhart household. John's elder brother James, was getting increasingly frustrated at John's antics. The incident at school when John had altered, and then discarded, James's best pair of trousers, was bad enough. There had never been any proof. But James knew exactly what had happened. The matter of the Health and Efficiency magazine was another issue for discussion.

Revenge was on the cards.

Chapter Twenty-Seven

802 L.A.C. Urquhart,
Air Movements Section,
R.A.F. Lyneham,
Nr. Swindon,
Wiltshire.

Mr J. Urquhart,
343 Laurel Avenue,
Inverness.
1 February 1958

Dear Dad,

It was wonderful to see you all. I find it hard to believe that I shall soon be in the desert.

Since my return I have been interviewed by the R.A.F. Special Investigation Branch, who are satisfied with my story about the magazine from Liverpool. I am so pleased that James has forgiven me, even if he did receive a twenty pound fine for receiving pornographic material through the post. I am sorry to hear that Norma Wallace has had a relapse, but that was no excuse for her father getting drunk at the church social. I am sure that his being expelled from the church will not affect his job. Good council clerks are hard to come by.

Lyneham is so different from West Kirby and Kidbrooke. There is less discipline. The work is hard. When I left Kidbrooke I thought that I would be sitting in an office, doing trim sheets and manifests, but the R.A.F. felt that my skills were more needed in loading aircraft. I cannot help feeling that this is fate. During the war, when you were in Burma, your duties involved loading aircraft. My aircraft are probably quite a bit bigger than the ones you worked on.

I should be promoted to Senior Aircraftsman next month. At this rate I expect to be an officer in about fifteen months.

Next week I shall be in the sun.
I am so excited.

Must close for now.
Duty calls.

Your loving son,
John Urquhart 802 L.A.C. (Soon to be S.A.C.)

Chapter Twenty-Eight

The Dan Air Bristol Britannia flew across the English Channel taking John to his new exciting life. An hour out of Stanstead Airport it was diverted to Nice Airport with engine trouble. Events were turning out as normal for John.

Nice Airport was full of glamour. Attractive air hostesses bustling about the terminal, and ravishing young film starlets fluttering past him, made John feel that he was in a new world. One of glamour. One that Alison would appreciate. The warmth and smell in the air made John feel heady. This was the life he could live. This was better than the Ferry. It was even better than Dalneigh.

The Britannia was delayed at Nice for four hours whilst repairs were effected. In that time John managed to send a postcard to his father. He also upset the local gendarmerie by asking, in schoolboy French, where the toilets were. It took John ten minutes, and a translator, to convince the gendarmes that he had not inferred that they looked like toilet cleaners.

This was John's first time on foreign soil. He recalled the number of films he had seen where the location had been the Cote D'Azur. He half-expected to run into some of his Hollywood idols. Had Doris Day been there he would probably have died on the spot.

It was night time when John arrived in Tripoli, North Africa. The heat on landing was oppressive. The smell different from anything he had ever experienced before.

His heart was pounding, with excitement and fear.

That night he shared a transit hut with five other young airmen, all overseas for the first time. They took it in turn to sleep. With a chair propped against the door to deny entry. But the sound of desert life denied sleep, even for those not detailed to stay awake.

At six o'clock the following morning there was a pounding on the door. John was on awake duty. He quickly awoke his half-sleeping companions, and they warily opened the door.

An Arab stood there.

The airmen huddled together.

"Your flight departs at nine o'clock," the well spoken Arab announced.

Chapter Twenty-Nine

John could see the barren wastes of desert below him, as the Eagle Airways D.C.3 aircraft droned steadily across the Libyan Desert.

Two hours before he had been sitting at Idris Airport, Tripoli, ready to board the scheduled Medair flight to Benina, El Adem and Cyprus. The passengers were all military personnel, with some in Army or Royal Navy uniform. The R.A.F. passengers, John included, wore civilian clothes, and each carried a British Passport declaring their occupation to be 'Government Official'. It made John feel incredibly important.

John boarded the aircraft. It was already occupied with passengers staging through from Malta. John sat next to a young lad in the uniform of the Royal Corps of Signals.

"It's a far cry from the Caley Park," said the voice next to him.

John looked at the young lad more closely. It was Jimmy Struthers from the Ferry. Jimmy was en-route from Malta to Benina. They spent the next hour catching up on home town gossip. Jimmy departed the aircraft at Benina.

The aircraft was only fifteen minutes flying time from El Adem when John began to smell smoke. Smoking was banned on the flight. There was no logical reason for the smell. But he waited before alerting anybody. He did not want to make a fool of himself.

John's seat was at the cockpit end of the aircraft, his

seat facing the rear, in military seating style. He was the passenger closest to the flight deck. By now he was sure he could smell smoke. Then he saw the tendrils of smoke wafting out of the electrical circuit panel.

John had a flashback to Dalneigh, when an over-enthusiastic squaw had set fire to the derelict farmhouse whilst playing cowboys and indians. John had thought he was going to die then. He recalled running from the farmhouse crying his eyes out.

He sat in his seat hoping that it was his imagination. If he closed his eyes it might go away. In the space of three minutes he discovered that he was in love with Alison from up the Hill, Mary from down the Ferry, the Barmaid from Swindon, the American Piper, and Moira the Vicar's Daughter. He even felt quite emotional about his neighbour, the one who wanted his body.

He thought of the only naked woman he had ever seen. Mrs Chrissie Forbes in 'The Sock Factory'. He had only been four years old. He would never know the touch or love of a woman.

He began to cry.

Chapter Thirty

The aircraft touched down at El Adem. The Fire Section stood by with both foam and water tenders, not sure what to expect. The emergency call from the aircraft had stated that there was an electrical fault on board, then communication had ceased altogether.

When the aircraft landed the fire engines got into position. It was essential that the aircraft be manoeuvred towards the holding area, at the far side of the airfield. The aircraft stopped. Within one minute all the passengers and crew had disembarked.

One minute later the aircraft was an inferno.

Fifteen minutes later John was in the passenger terminal. Apart from the civilian clothes he stood up in, he had no possessions. His service kit had been destroyed in the fire. Within a few hours he was freshly kitted out. He was issued with desert kit, including shorts. He had not worn a pair of shorts since his first week at the Technical School.

He reported to the Air Movements section and was introduced to his new work colleagues. He was allocated a bed in a tent shared with five other airmen.

The heat was intense. The smell was overpowering.

'The smell,' it was explained by one of his new tent-mates "is chlorine from the drinking water, combined with the stench from the open latrines."

The smell for some strange reason made John feel homesick. Then he realised why. It reminded him of "Jock's Kitchen."

The morning after arrival at El Adem, John reported for duty in the Movements Section. There was little activity. There were only two scheduled flights a week. These were both Eagle Airways D.C.3 runs, call-sign 'Medair', the very flight that John had arrived on. An occasional R.A.F. Hercules, Britannia or Beverley aircraft, would stage through en-route to Aden and the Far East.

As one of the more cynical of his new work-mates summarised. "Welcome to El Adem. You are just commencing the most boring two years of your life. If you leave here sane and without a serious drink problem it will be a miracle."

John's thoughts of excitement vanished.

On his first day of duty John queried why there were five depressed aircrew officers sitting in the transit lounge.

"They're not depressed," he was advised. "They're suicidal. They've been sitting here for a week with their Beverley. Some imbecile at Lyneham drove a forklift through the replacement spares. It's going to take a week to get the new spares here. The Medical Officer is already concerned. The Navigator, Flight Lieutenant Robson-Stuart, proposed to the co-pilot yesterday, and got quite upset when he was rejected. Apparently the Special Investigation Branch are investigating the AOG spares incident. They'll get the nitwit who did it eventually."

John completed his shift that day and strolled back to his tent. The vehicle used for emptying the contents of the latrines passed him, heading into the desert to unload its contents. As though orchestrated, the chlorine tanker passed at the same time, proceeding into the camp to top up the drinking water supplies.

That evening John stood outside his tent looking across the desert. The scenery was bleak, with scrub replacing his pre-conceived vision of sand dunes. He thought of Inverness, of the Ness Islands. The contrast was unbelievable.

He had joined the R.A.F. in the hope of travel, excitement, and a girl friend. He now found himself on a planet of desolation, with no potential girlfriends within several hundred miles. He was stuck in the desert for the next two years.

He was so depressed that he completely forgot that in the previous three days he had been on an aircraft that had been diverted through engine trouble, an aircraft that had caught fire, and he was now probably chief suspect, in fact probably sole suspect, in the AOG incident at Lyneham.

He hoped the investigation police would arrive at El Adem after the Beverley crew had left.

He did not fancy being pursued by a frustrated rejected Navigator, who would be even more agitated when he discovered that John was the culprit.

Chapter Thirty-One

John did not have to wait long for the investigators to arrive. They arrived at El Adem three days later on a Britannia from Lyneham. Co-incidentally, the new spares for the Beverley were on the same flight.

But it was not the fork-lift incident the investigators wanted to discuss. There was another, but equally serious question, directed at John.

"Are you 802 L.A.C. Urquhart?" the first service investigator asked.

John thought this was rather a stupid question as he had just been introduced by his Flight Commander.

"Is this your signature?" the second Snowdrop asked, showing John an aircraft equipment sheet.

John looked at the equipment sheet, wondering where this was all leading.

John acknowledged that it was his signature.

The first plod stood up.

"Right," he began, "we can do this the easy way, or the hard way. What have you done with the search beacon?"

John looked at the policemen and wondered what the hell they were talking about.

"What are you talking about?" John asked, speaking his thoughts aloud.

"I see. Playing the innocent, are we?" detective one remarked. "You signed-off the search beacon on the arrival of this aircraft at Lyneham on December 23rd. What did you do with it?"

John looked at the equipment sheet again. His signature was there. He thought back to the 23rd of December. The date rang a bell. Then it hit him.

He had been on night shift at Lyneham, but had attended a party in the N.A.A.F.I. early in the evening. He had a few drinks at the party and had then reported for duty. There was only one aircraft arrival that night. This had allowed the rest of the shift to stand down to begin early Christmas leave.

He thought through the sequence of events.

The aircraft had landed. He had gone out to check the equipment. The role-equipment team had turned up to configure the aircraft in the role required for its next flight. John had removed the Search and Rescue Beacon and he had… then it dawned on him. He had wanted to get back to the party in the N.A.A.F.I. In order to save time he had placed the search beacon in the back of the role equipment vehicle. Normal standard practice.

Only this time it wasn't normal practice.

The difference this time was that most of the role equipment team had also stood down early for Christmas. They also were cutting corners. Instead of the normal three ton truck to offload the safety equipment, they had used a refuse cart. John remembered it vividly. The search and rescue beacon went into the back of the dustcart, along with all the other safety equipment and catering containers.

John had returned to the party in the N.A.A.F.I., and completely forgot that he should have checked the equipment back into stores the following morning.

It dawned on John, whilst he was being interrogated, that all the equipment from the flight had probably ended up in a landfill site in Swindon.

The interrogation had been underway only thirty minutes when it was abruptly brought to a halt. The investigators had decided to leave El Adem for Aden on the Britannia they arrived on.

The interview would have continued longer, but the investigators decided to abort when the Britannia navigator, Flight Lieutenant Robson-Stuart, began to caress the smaller of the two investigators.

It did not matter to the investigators that they were not scheduled to travel to Aden. Flight Lieutenant Robson-Stuart had made it quite clear that he would stay in El Adem as long as they were there.

The whole Air Force knew of the Flight Lieutenant's reputation.

Chapter Thirty-Two

Paddy Ryan, the Orderly Sergeant, was convinced he was going mad. He slowed down the Landrover and stopped some fifty yards from the crashed Canberra. He quietly got out of the vehicle and slowly crept towards the aircraft.

He paused a few feet from his objective. There was no doubt about it. He could hear singing. He struggled to make out the words. They did not make sense. A feeling of recognition came over him as he realised that he had heard the words to the song some forty years before. He undid his holster and, gun in hand, stepped out from behind the aircraft. He could not believe what he saw and heard.

"A Sunbeam, a Sunbeam, Jesus wants me for a Sunbeam," the voice was singing.

Standing there, stark naked, with his back to the sergeant, and totally oblivious to his presence, John stood, clutching his rifle in the 'Halt who goes there?' position.

"Have you gone bloody mad, Urquhart?" the sergeant asked, not quite sure what the reply would be.

John wheeled to face the sergeant.

The bullet missed the sergeant by a matter of inches and struck the Landrover. There was a roar as the petrol-tank caught fire.

It had all begun when John, after only thirty days at El Adem, was detailed to guard a Canberra bomber which had crashed in the desert thirty miles from the airbase. John was issued with a .303 rifle and five rounds of ammunition. For the first time ever he was in possession of live ammunition.

He was driven out by landrover to the site of the crash. His instructions were to stay there, in the shade of the aircraft, and allow nobody near the aircraft. There was desert as far as the eye could see in all directions.

John sat down and closed his eyes.

Forty-five minutes later he awoke, startled, wondering why he felt so hot, when he thought he was sitting in a cafe in Inverness having an ice cream soda which had been served by a sultry waitress who could not take her eyes off him.

Twenty yards from him was a spectacle John had only read about in books. A camel train, with twenty Bedouin tribesmen, was crossing in front of the crashed Canberra.

John jump to his feet, by now fully awake

"Holy Mary, mother of God!" he muttered to himself before he remembered he was not Catholic. "What do I do?"

As though assisting him in reaching an answer to the question, one of the nomads detached himself from the train and approached John. The Arab had an ancient rifle strapped across his chest. The remaining nomads each had an ancient rifle, all pointed at John.

John counted his bullets. Five. He counted the travellers. Twenty. He was fifteen bullets short. But did it matter? At the West Kirby rifle range he had missed the target each time.

John pointed the rifle towards the oncoming traveller.

"Halt, who goes there, friend or foe?" asked John, suddenly remembering his guard duty training.

The question was superfluous.

The Bedouin smiled at John and reeled off several words in Arabic.

John stood his ground. He had no choice. He had no idea what the Arab had said. He was frozen to the spot.

The matter was resolved when the Arab held his hand out to John in a gesture of friendship. John slowly extended his hand. They shook hands. The Arab walked back to the camel train and spoke to his fellow travellers, They all looked at John and collectively burst into gales of laughter.

John had wet himself.

John stood there as the camel train departed. He would not make the same mistake again. He would keep his rifle in his hands at all times.

Five minutes after the camel train had departed he stopped shaking. He stripped off his shirt, soaked in sweat, and his shorts which were soaked in urine. He draped them over the fuselage of the aircraft.

John had experienced an unnerving incident. In the past when this had happened – the Mary Wilson incident after the Kirtarlity dance was a good example, John had sought the comfort of his Christian upbringing. He searched his mind for a thought of comfort, or a prayer, or a hymn. 'Onwards Christian Soldiers' crossed his mind, as did 'Fight the Good Fight'.

But John had seen enough military action for one day.

Then he remembered his Sunday School days.

John was on his third rendition of 'A Sunbeam', standing naked, and oblivious to anything else, when he heard the voice behind him. He turned around, gun at his shoulder, and fired. The Landrover burst into flames as the bullet hit the petrol tank.

Eight hours later Flight Lieutenant Smythe, the orderly officer, arrived at the site of the crashed Canberra. He was accompanied by three airmen, all fully armed. Concern had arisen back at El Adem when it was realised that the guard change-over had not been executed on time, and the orderly sergeant was missing.

It had taken the orderly corporal four hours to find the orderly officer. He was eventually found in a bed in the sick bay. With a bottle of Port, and the Records Clerk from station headquarters.

Cautiously the officer and airmen approached the crashed aircraft. Beside the aircraft was a burnt out Landrover. The officer paused. He could hear voices.

"All Things Bright and Beautiful," the voices sang in harmony from behind the Canberra.

The orderly officer could not believe his eyes. Sitting in the sand were the figures of L.A.C. Urquhart and the orderly sergeant. They were both naked, although Sergeant Paddy Ryan had his shirt loosely draped about the top half of his body. Hanging from the fuselage of the aircraft was two pairs of underpants (drawers cellular), two pairs of khaki drill shorts, and a shirt.

It transpired that when John had fired the shot, the sergeant, thinking that John had gone mad and was trying to kill him, immediately wet himself.

The effect of sitting out in the sun with no water for eight hours, and John's repeated singing of Sunday School songs, had reduced the sergeant to a nervous wreck.

John was sentenced to thirty days confinement to camp for having 'a bullet up the breech of his rifle when there was no danger'.

The sergeant spent thirty days in sickbay, and became a confirmed atheist.

Chapter Thirty-Three

802 S.A.C. Urquhart,
Air Movements Section,
R.A.F. El Adem,
B.F.P,O. 56
10 March 1958

Mr J. Urquhart,
343 Laurel Avenue,
Inverness.

Dear Dad,

Well as you can see I am now overseas, and promoted to Senior Aircraftsman. Before I go on with my news I must say that I am surprised to hear that Norma Wallace has left home at the age of fourteen to work as a model. She must be the youngest model in Britain. I expect my magazine gave her the incentive.

I flew out to Libya in a Britannia aircraft belonging to Dan Air from Stanstead Airport in Essex. I half expected to see the Mekon on the flight (Dan Dare – the Eagle Comic, get it). As you will realise from my postcard, we landed at Nice because of engine trouble. It was a smashing flight, much better than the Beverley aircraft, although I think I preferred the Beverley parachute seats.

I spent the first night in Tripoli with some other lads who were overseas for the first time. We had a great time exploring the surrounding area before we departed for El Adem the next day.

An amazing coincidence, I met Jimmy Struthers on the flight. You know his parents. They live in Craigton Avenue, or at least they do when Mr Struthers is not in prison, and Mrs Struthers is not in Craig Dunain. I never have liked Jimmy. I am sure he is the one who told the teacher at the Kessock School that I was the mastermind behind the school bell incident.

Well, if engine failure on the Britannia to Tripoli was not enough, on the D.C.3 flight to El Adem the plane caught fire. I am sure if it was not for my quick thinking we would all be dead. I alerted the crew to the problem and helped to put out the fire.

Oh, I forgot to mention by the way that I was driving whilst at Lyneham. It was only a forklift, but it's a start.

I was on guard duty for a few days when I first arrived. A jet on a bombing mission had crashed in the desert, and I had to guard it with my .303 and real ammunition. I spoke to some Arabs who passed by with camels. I have already picked up a few words of Arabic, so we communicated quite well.

Well, that's all the news for now Dad. The camp is quite nice. I share a tent with five other lads. Just like The Boys Brigade.

Your loving son,
John Urquhart 802 S.A.C.

P.S. I'm pleased that Sandy Roberts sees you a lot and you tell him how exciting my life is. Tell James and the family that I miss them.

Chapter Thirty-Four

S.A.C. Urquhart,
Air Movements Squadron,
B.F.P.O.56

Miss Alison Forbes,
Hill House,
Up the Hill, Inverness.
30 March 1958

My Dearest Alison,

Thank you for the wonderful letter. I am so pleased that you are missing me. I cannot describe how much I would like to be with you.

I flew out of the UK a couple of weeks ago for this secret destination. It is safe for me to tell you that the aircraft staged through Nice, in the south of France. I saw a few famous film stars in the airport lounge. I think you and I would enjoy being there. Somehow I feel we would fit in with the rest of the people. It gave me an opportunity to speak a great deal of French.

Where am I, you might ask. Well, it is secret, but it is hot, and there are lots of films made here. I work closely with the U.S.A.F. That means United States Air Force. But no more hints, or I will find myself in serious trouble.

As you can see I am now a Senior Air Controller. I am responsible for the aircraft operations at this airfield. It is an important job and I thoroughly enjoy controlling the staff.

I know that you felt badly that I did not follow through my intention to be a brain-surgeon, but I really did feel that I could be of more benefit to everybody by helping to make the world a safer place. It is no easy task.

I hope that your nurses training is going well. Please give my regards to your grandmother. I am sure I will see her one day.

I am now into classical music in a big way. I love Beethoven. I have decided that on my return we must try and see My Fair Lady. I know the show is on in London, but it would be a lovely reason for us to have our first time away together. Every time I hear 'On the street where you live' I recall the wonderful time when we first met, when I walked you home from the dance in the Nurse's Home.

Well, I must go now. Remember to keep away from the rough council estates.

All my love,
Thinking of you every day,

Johnny XXX

Chapter Thirty-Five

Eight weeks after arriving at El Adem John boarded a three ton truck which did a twice daily run between the military garrisons at Tobruk and El Adem.

The journey to Tobruk was through countryside similar to the Highlands of Scotland. All that was missing was the greenery, the mountains, the rivers, and signs of civilisation. As compensation there was the desert, the scrub, the burnt out vehicles from the Second World War, the desert, and yet more desert.

John had never seen such a desolate place.

Even Wales was more appealing.

The town of Tobruk was still a bombsite from the effects of the siege during the Second World War. There was hardly a building that had not been damaged to some degree. There was an air of depression about the place. John could not believe the living conditions. He wondered how people could possibly live there.

Over the following months John settled into what passed for a normal life routine at El Adem. This mainly consisted of drinking in the N.A.A.F.I. with his colleagues, trying to forget where they were, and calculating the days until their return to Blighty, as they affectionately called the UK.

Personal possessions for the airmen were sparse. John's tent mates did however have the luxury of a record player. But only three records. Songs by Julie London, lyrics from the stage show 'My Fair Lady' and Beethoven.

The same music ran through John's mind day after day. On hearing Beethoven, John frequently wished that he was at home in Dalneigh, hearing his sister play 'God Save the Queen' as she practised on the Sunday School piano, using two fingers.

Depression was the common thread bonding the airmen together. The airmen's spirits were lifted when one of them reached the end of their tour of duty. This meant a new arrival with more time to do than any of them. The tedium was not helped by the low work activity. With only two scheduled flights a week, and the odd R.A.F. aircraft using the base as a staging post to Aden or Singapore there was time to sit and brood.

Guard duties came around with regular monotony. It was no different from any other day, apart from being unable to use the bar facilities in the N.A.A.F.I.

Whilst on guard duty, lying awake in the middle of the night, (the expression 'alert and awake' could never be used), John would hear the drone of an aircraft flying several thousand feet above him. He wondered where it had come from, and where it was going.

Once a week a film would be shown in the station cinema. Without fail the film would be preceded by a cartoon. When the name of the cartoon producer, Fred Quimby, appeared at the end of the five minute nonsense, the whole cinema would give a standing ovation to shouts of 'Good Old Fred'. It was a way of relieving the tension of frustration and boredom. It was also a touch of madness.

Friday evenings in the N.A.A.F.I. were 'Dear John' occasions. In front of an assembly of very drunken compatriots the recipient of a 'Dear John' letter would pin the letter to the dartboard. A 'Dear John' letter was a letter advising that a relationship had ended. The lonely girl left behind was no longer alone.

All the airmen took turns to throw darts at the letter. It was another way of relieving stress.

At the end of the evening the recipient of the 'Dear John' would crawl back to his tent, all bravado gone, crying his eyes out.

But idle hands and frustration are key elements for mischief. Every opportunity was seized when harmless mischief could be exploited.

John was on duty when Beverley aircraft XJ404, en route to Aden, stopped in transit at El Adem. Parked alongside the Aden bound Beverley was Beverley XJ392 bound for Cyprus. It was a rare busy day in the movements section. Staging through on the Aden flight was the senior officer that John had encountered in the bar at Lyneham on the previous Christmas Eve. The one with the seventy-five year old mother-in-law.

At the subsequent enquiry, John's shift controller had the task of explaining to the senior movements officer, how the baggage for the Aden bound Squadron Leader had arrived in Cyprus. John shrugged his shoulders when asked, and gestured to the local labour force.

Customs-seized cigarettes were issued free to all the airmen. John found a good market for these. There was always somebody who wanted to purchase John's free allocation. It was illegal to do so. But occasions arose when the odd guard duty, or fire picket, could be avoided, with a bribe of two hundred cigarettes.

The same bribe worked with local labourers when favours were required on loading aircraft.

Chapter Thirty-Six

John had been at El Adem six months, and was on duty meeting an inbound flight when he heard a voice utter the words, "Johnny Urquhart, I thought I'd find you here."

John was confronted by the grinning face of Sandy Roberts, his old 'Kessie' chum.

That evening, over a few beers, John and Sandy exchanged news. Sandy had stayed on at his survey job for a further ten months after John had joined the R.A.F. Sandy had received his National Service call up papers and, even though he could have been deferred as he was learning a trade, he decided to enlist in the R.A.F. to do his two years National Service.

John's enthusiastic letters to his father, extolling the good life that John was having, was the clincher for Sandy. John had been experiencing all the excitement that Sandy was missing. Or so he had thought.

Despite John's letters to his father saying how easy he had found square-bashing, information passed to Sandy by John's father, Sandy had actually found the square-bashing extremely hard. Based on the glowing reports in John's letters, Sandy had also enrolled in the trade of Air Movements. Again he had found that this was not quite what John had explained in his letters home.

Sandy was very forgiving however, to the point that he passed on a message from John's brother James.

"It appears," Sandy stated, "that an old acquaintance of yours, Nurse Lesley Graham, saw you at the Nurses'

Home dance. James suggests that you write to Lesley."

John was delighted. Apart from his father, and Alison, he had nobody else to write to. He was also having great difficulty keeping up the pretence to Alison, about precisely what his role in the R.A.F. was. Being asked to write to Lesley was what he needed. He recalled the dance in the Nurses' Home, and the glimpse of the beautiful girl who smiled as he left.

In appreciation of Sandy's gesture, John insisted that he show Sandy the delights of Tobruk the following day.

By the time they went to bed that night, they had discussed every girl in Inverness. For both of them the position was the same. However, despite the desperate efforts they had made, neither of them had anything remotely resembling a real girlfriend. Sandy consoled a tearful and very drunken John.

"Do yourself a favour. Write to Nurse Lesley Graham tomorrow."

Chapter Thirty-Seven

John and Sandy caught the three-ton truck to Tobruk the following day. Neither of them were feeling particularly bright, thanks to over-consumption the night before. John had also insisted on writing to Nurse Lesley Graham before he fell asleep. The Medair mail flight was due that day and he wanted to make sure his letter was not delayed. He desperately wanted to hear from this nurse who knew so much about him.

By mid-day they were in Tobruk. They were dropped off and reminded that the vehicle would return to El Adem at four o'clock that afternoon. This gave them four hours to explore Tobruk.

Thirty minutes later the tour was complete. Most of the thirty minutes consisted of trying to convince a street urchin, who looked about five years old, that they were not interested in buying dirty photographs of his sister. The decision not to buy was made after looking at the photographs. John was in two minds, he had been in the desert longer than Sandy. But Sandy convinced him otherwise. On hearing their decision the young boy gave a two-fingered salute, accompanied with verbal insults about 'British pigs'.

A strip of desert ran along the coast of North Africa leading down to the Mediterranean sea. The beach was three miles from Tobruk. John had the day all planned, Down to the beach, taking along with them the cans of Amstel purchased from the N.A.A.F.I. the night before.

The picnic ingredients were in a plastic bag. Twelve cans of Amstel. Nothing else.

To get to the beach however they had to hire bicycles.

The bicycle shop owner greeted them warmly, and, with hand gestures, invited them to pick their choice of bicycle. The last time John had seen a similar collection of bicycles was down the Ferry, courtesy of the medical profession. Clearly the skills of the Ferry kids had spread world-wide.

The bicycles selected, the shop owner pointed to a scruffy notebook and indicated that the boys should sign for the bicycles. Sandy put his hand in his pocket for his R.A.F. Identity Card but he was stopped by John.

"We don't need those, it's all on trust." John stated as he signed the hire-book.

Sandy picked up the pen and looked at John's entry in the book.

'Mickey Mouse', the signature read.

Sandy was no fool. He wrote under John's entry 'Donald Duck'.

Twenty minutes later the boys were on the beach. There was nobody else in sight. Neither of them could swim. They opened a can of lager each. And then another can.

It was half past four in the afternoon when John awoke, realised what the time was and woke Sandy. The drink, and lack of sleep on the previous night, had taken their toll. They mounted their bicycles, praying that the lorry had not left for El Adem.

It had.

The dejected duo, leaning on their bicycles, gazed at the empty road leading out of Tobruk. Vehicles here were rarer than in Dalneigh in 1951.

"What do we do now?" asked a concerned Sandy. He

had not been out in the desert long enough to appreciate that this was not a problem, it was an opportunity.

John pondered the dilemma for a moment and arrived at what he believed the only sensible solution. The solution brainwashed into Ferry folk over decades.

"Let's go for a drink," he stated.

Fifteen minutes later the duo were comfortably seated in the Corporals Club at Tobruk Garrison having refreshments. Sandy's concern at using a club they should not have been in was dismissed by John. Sandy could see that something had changed in John since their Inverness days. John was no longer the shy timid weakling he had been in Inverness. John was not only more assertive. He actually seemed to enjoy confrontation.

The confrontation arose when they were asked for their identity.

The lads were thrown out of the Corporals Club.

The Oasis Hotel, a three star slum, was the only non-military establishment in Tobruk providing rooms and alcohol. The lads, by now fairly drunk, found themselves sitting in the basement bar of the hotel.

The sign at the entrance of the hotel stated 'Out of Bounds to British ranks. Officers only'. John, completely unfazed, sauntered into the hotel as though he owned it. He had the experience of entering the Caley Ballroom behind him. As far as John was concerned an 'Out of Bounds' sign meant that there was some excitement going on.

An 'Out of Bounds' sign was probably the most effective advertisement ever devised to lure young servicemen. It was the equivalent of the finger of Mary Wilson's mother, beckoning from the Harbour Inn.

The belly-dancer was more belly than dancer. Sitting on the large pouffe was not Sandy's idea of fun, but John, got into the mood very quickly. The last time he had seen this much flesh was in the usherettes changing room at the Playhouse Cinema. Where Sandy saw Fat, John saw Fantastic.

The boys sat there for an hour, each nursing a whisky cocktail that had cost a day's wages. At the end of the hour, the proprietor realising that the boys were unlikely to buy another drink, even if the belly dancer stripped naked, had them thrown out of the hotel.

As John picked himself off the pavement, he fell against the hire bicycles, which had been parked outside the hotel. He considered mounting the bicycle but, like father, like son, decided to push the bicycle at an angle of forty-five degrees. When they arrived at the cycle hire shop they discovered that it was closed.

But John was resourceful. He knew of yet another drinking establishment in Tobruk. Yet another 'Out of Bounds' establishment. It was a bar operated by German ex-prisoners of war, who had stayed on in North Africa after the Second World War. The Germans had set up a building maintenance company, and were executing repairs to British military bases. Putting right, at great cost, the damage they had done.

But let bygones be bygones. The Germans were a hospitable crowd until midnight.

By that time John and Sandy had consumed a crate of Amstel and a bottle of Johnny Walker, all on credit. The altercation came when, quite reasonably, the German barman requested payment, as the bar was about to close.

John offered two bicycles as payment.

This was rejected.

The lads were ejected.

The last thing Sandy saw, and heard, was John being thrown out the open window of the German Club, singing as he went, "Close the doors, they're coming out the windows."

John was found lying across some barbed wire which was at the top of the wall leading into Tobruk Garrison. Sandy was found in the Oasis Hotel. He had been arrested after phoning the Garrison guardroom, stating that he was a Squadron Leader and demanding John's release. It took the Military Police ten minutes to figure out where Sandy was phoning from. It would have taken all night if one of the cell occupants, on overhearing the debate, had not pointed out that the only working telephone in Tobruk, other than those in the military garrison, was in the Oasis Hotel.

John awoke the worse for wear. He had trouble focussing, but had the feeling that he was in a prison cell. He could not find his spectacles. His shoelaces and belt were also missing. The absence of his spectacles created serious problems. It was bad enough being half-drunk, as he still was, but being half blind as well was just too much to cope with.

He hammered on the door of the cell. He was confident now that it was a cell.

The door was opened by a military policeman.

John and Sandy, escorted by a Redcap in front and one behind, were marched to the Station Commander's office to the cheers, and jeers, of a crowd of local Arabs. A young lad, about five years of age, stuck two fingers in the air as the airmen marched past. The boy was straddling two bicycles.

Sandy's charge of 'being drunk and disorderly and impersonating an officer' was read first. Sandy was sentenced to seven days detention, and confinement to camp for a further thirty days. He had only been at El Adem for forty-eight hours.

167

There was a delay in reading John's charge whilst John composed himself. The military policeman reading out the charges on Sandy had got as far as 'impersonating' when John collapsed, hysterical with laughter.

John had thought the policeman was going to say 'impersonating Mickey Mouse and Donald Duck'.

John was found five shillings for being drunk and disorderly. There was no record available at the Tobruk Garrison of his previous offences at West Kirby, Lyneham and El Adem.

On the way to his cell for his seven-day holiday Sandy remarked to John. "Not to worry, mate. It's just one of those things."

John was moved. In the space of forty-eight hours, his best friend had given him the address of a nurse who wanted to write to him, and by way of thanks John had got Sandy in trouble.

John vowed to make it up to Sandy.

Chapter Thirty-Eight

802 S.A.C. Urquhart
Air Movements Section,
R.A.F. El Adem,
B.F.P.O.56

Nurse Lesley Graham,
Nurses Home.
Royal Northern Infirmary.
Inverness.

10 September 1958

Dear Lesley,

Sandy Roberts has just given me your name and asked that I write to you. I understand from Sandy that you saw me at a dance at the Nurses' Home. I see that you live in the home.

Have you been nursing long? Are you from Inverness? There is so much that we have to tell each other. I do hope that you would like to write to me, and that this is not another of Sandy's wind-ups.

El Adem is a miserable God forsaken place completely out of touch with the modern world. I cannot begin to describe the living conditions. I live in a tent with five other airmen. There is barely enough room to swing a cat.

There is not a great deal to do, as there are only a few

aircraft flights each week. We tend to wander around camp wearing our K.D. shorts and nothing else. I should end up with a good sun tan.

Well, Lesley, I am not sure what else to say. When I hear from you I will be able to write a longer letter.

Please write soon,
Your friend.

Johnny

Chapter Thirty-Nine

802 S.A.C. Urquhart,
Air Movements Section
R.A.F. El Adem,
B.F.P.O. 56

Nurse Lesley Graham,
Nurses Home,
Royal Northern Infirmary,
Inverness.

20 September 1958

Dear Lesley,

It was great to hear from you. I have never had a reply to a letter so quickly. Usually the mail takes a week to get here from the UK.

You are the first person I have met who was born on the Isle of Skye. I have never been to Skye, but I hear that it is a lovely place. I am pleased that you enjoy nursing. I think that it is a wonderful profession, full of dedicated people.

You asked what my hobbies are. Well I like music, but not classical. We have only three records in our tent, and although I like the voice of Julie London, I find both the dirge of Beethoven, and the music from My Fair Lady, a bit overpowering.

You are right in thinking that it is nice to be sharing a

tent with my five mates, but there is just no room for privacy. They are great company in the evening, when we have quite a few drinks in the N.A.A.F.I.

Sandy and I had a smashing time in Tobruk last week. We had a few drinks too many, and ended up in trouble with the Military Police. Still, boys will be boys.

I shall finish this now as I want to drop it in the mail sack. This letter will go out on the same flight as yours arrived on.

I shall write a much longer letter next time.

Please, please, write soon. I think we could get on quite well.

Fondest regards,

Johnny
XX

p.s. I had no idea that you knew my brother James.

Chapter Forty

Christmas 1958 dawned, and with it the news that John was to make his debut as a radio presenter the following week.

The Radio Station T.E.A.R.S. (Tobruk and El Adem Radio Station), which provided entertainment to some of the military bases in North Africa, had asked John to present the New Year's Eve programme.

The selection of John to perform the task had been fairly simple, once the concept had been accepted. The programme producer had expressed the view that a Scottish touch to New Year's Eve would be appropriate. The producer was a pilot officer in the R.A.F. Equipment Branch. He was from the Chelsea area of London, had gone to a public school, and had frequently made the point of condemning the Scots as being boorish.

The request, by the producer, for a Scots announcer to present the New Year's Eve programme was made at the December meeting of the programme planners. When the idea was mooted there were gasps around the table. The station had achieved a great deal of credibility. They were not happy at taking risks.

The pilot officer advised the programmers that the matter was not really up for discussion. The Tobruk garrison commander had pointed out that New Year's Eve was of particular interest to the Scots, and as there was a Battalion of the Gordon Highlanders conducting desert training in the area, it would be a nice touch to have a

Scottish theme to Hogmanay.

This prompted the pilot officer producer to raise the question. "Who do we get to present the programme?"

It was the Records Clerk from station headquarters who came up with the John's name. The clerk had been in the N.A.A.F.I. on several occasions during the previous week. On each occasion he had heard the Air Movers drunken rabble singing.

The singsong on each occasion had started with one particularly loud and obnoxious voice proclaiming, "I Belong To Glasgow". This was followed by other songs which the clerk could not understand, but he felt sure they were Scottish.

The Records Clerk was keen to put forward John's name for the task as he was the same clerk who had a delightful afternoon spoiled when Flight Lieutenant Smythe, the orderly officer, was called out over the crashed Canberra incident when John was on guard duty. The clerk and the orderly officer were well into a bottle of Port, swapping stories on life in an all-boys school, when the call came. The clerk had abstained from drink since the incident.

The clerk's recommendation for John to be the programme producer was not a gesture of reconciliation. The Records Clerk was convinced that John would make a complete fool of himself.

On New Year's Eve, 1958, having consumed eight Tom Collins (John was experimenting with cocktails at this stage), the voice of John Urquhart was heard in the military garrisons at Tobruk, El Adem, and other military bases in North Africa..

John introduced one hour of Scottish music to bring in the New Year. On completion of his Scottish repertoire, he played a special piece of music for his tent-mates.

When the familiar, all too familiar, sound of Beethoven's Piano Concerto No. 5 in E flat Major, came over the airwaves, wails of anguish, and screams, could be heard coming from John's tent.

This was matched by the screams of rage from the Tobruk Garrison when John played 'Donald Where's Your Troosers?' for The Gordon Highlanders. A riot broke out between the Gordons and the R.A.F. men in the garrison.

John's radio career lasted exactly one hour.

Chapter Forty-One

802 Cpl. Urquhart,
Air Movements Section
R.A.F. El Adem,
B.F.P.O. 56

Mr J. Urquhart,.
343 Laurel Avenue,
Inverness.

5 January 1959

Dear Dad,

First the excellent news. I am now a Corporal. The big event happened on Christmas Eve so I had a lovely Birthday and Christmas present. I am in charge of a team of eight airmen. I should be a good Corporal, as I command respect from my team.

I had a very quiet Christmas. On Christmas Day we had lunch in the Airmens' Mess. Lunch was served by the officers. We gave them a vote of thanks after the meal.

Sandy and I are good company for each other. It is bloody awful here. I am sorry for the language but there is no other way to describe it. I have been here nearly a year (only 420 days to go). I try not to let it get me down.

The most exciting news of all however is that I am now a radio star. Wee Johnny Urquhart, your son and heir, brought in the New Year on the Forces Radio in the

Middle East. I think I was picked because our Inverness English is regarded as the most perfect in the world.

I had not mentioned it before but I am writing to several girls at once. You have heard me mention Alison (from up the Hill). I am engaged to Alison but I now also write to Lesley, who is also a nurse, and a girl called Jessica, who is a dancer in Glasgow.

I am really pleased that James keeps sending his regards. I am looking forward to seeing him. I wonder what the surprise is that he says he has for me. I am lucky to have him as a brother.

I expect to go to Malta in the next few weeks. You will remember that I guarded a crashed aircraft when I first arrived at El Adem. The Canberra Squadron is showing their appreciation by taking two of the recovery team in one of their bombers. I have never been to Malta, and have never been in a bomber, so it should be quite exciting.

Will close now.

Your loving son,

CORPORAL John Urquhart (sounds good doesn't it?)

Chapter Forty-Two

S.A.C. J. Urquhart.
Air Movements Squadron
B.F.P.O. 56

Miss Alison Forbes,
Hill House,
Up The Hill,
Inverness.

5 January 1959

My Darling Alison,

I was thrilled to receive your wonderful letter on Christmas Eve. I have never before received a card on my birthday addressed to 'My Darling Fiancé'.

I have two pieces of exciting news. I have been promoted but I cannot reveal, for security reasons, what my new rank is. The next piece of exciting news is that I have presented a show on the radio. The show, entitled 'An Evening With John and his Favourite Music', was broadcast on Forces Radio world-wide. I played a Beethoven piece which I just know you would love.

Christmas was very peaceful. I attended a church service. I am in a different location from when I last wrote to you, but I cannot say where for security reasons. This is the fourth country I have been to within the past six months. I am certainly seeing the world.

I had a wonderful lunch in the Officers Mess on Christmas Day. They somehow knew that it was my Birthday and I received a vote of thanks from my fellow officers.

There are so many things I want us to do when I return. I miss you so much. You are the only girl for me. I have found my soul mate.

There is another chap from Inverness at my present station. He is pleasant enough although merely an airman. But he is not like you or I. I have a feeling he was born in the Ferry district. There is something not quite right about him.

I will be flying to yet another destination in a few weeks, this time in a bomber as part of the crew. I hope I have not revealed any secrets by telling you that.

Take care, my darling fiancée,
All my love,

John

P.S. I had no idea that you did not like the name 'Johnny'. I agree with you that it is a bit common. I shall not use it again.
XXXXX

Chapter Forty-Three

802 Corporal J. Urquhart
Air Movements Section
R.A.F. El Adem,
B.F.P.O. 56

Nurse Lesley Graham,
Nurses Home, Royal Northern Infirmary,
Inverness.

5 January 1959

My Dearest Lesley,

It hardly seems possible that we have been writing to each other for only a few months. I feel that I have known you all my life. We have so much in common.

Note the new rank by the way. I am now a Corporal and can give any punishment I want. A weak joke, but I feel I can be frivolous with you.

Christmas day was quiet. I had a combined birthday lunch and Christmas lunch in the Airmen's Mess. It was a bit tacky, with two hundred drunken airmen fighting over what allegedly was turkey.

I am looking forward so much to seeing you. I know it is still a long time until January next year, but I will make sure we have a good time when I see you.

You asked about the living conditions here. Well as you know, not only do I share a tent with five other

*airmen, but there is not even any privacy in the showers. I
don't know why they call them showers. We stand in a long
row, whilst a native Arab pours water down a chute. There
is then a terrible scramble to get underneath the water.*

*Did you go to the Caley last week, I have only been to
one Christmas dance there, but it was terrific. I hope you
were not chatted up by any drunken airmen from Kinloss,
or worse still, one of the kilted mob.*

*The dance at the Nurses' Home sounded good fun. Did
you bring a boyfriend? I do hope not. I have a feeling that
we are getting quite close, and I can feel a tinge of
jealousy.*

*If it is any help in making me sound more important,
you can tell your friends that you are writing to a real live
radio announcer. Yes. I presented my own record show on
New Year's Eve on the local armed forces radio station. It
was good fun. I played a record just for you.*

*I miss you so much. That sounds silly as we have not
met, but you know what I mean.*

Please keep writing, daily if you can.

I do so love hearing from you.

Love.

Johnny.

Chapter Forty-Four

802 Cpl. Urquhart J.
Air Movements Section,
R.A.F. El Adem,
B.F.P.O.56

Miss Jessica Rawlings,
The Ship Inn,
Dock Road,
Clydeside,
Glasgow.

5 January 1959

Dear Jessica,

I am writing this letter in response to your request in the Tit-Bits for pen-friends. I know that you asked for sailor pen-friends. As you can see I am not in the Navy but I would like to write to you. It is very lonely out here. It is always good to hear from new friends.

I have only been in Glasgow once. This was when I had finished my square-bashing in Liverpool. I stopped off for a drink in a bar just outside Queen Street Station. I met a few nice people there. I really must spend more time in Glasgow when I get back to Scotland.

I work in the Air Movements Section. It is not as glamorous as it sounds. The work consists of loading and unloading aircraft. More like a ships docker really. Living near the Glasgow Docks you will know what I mean.

I note from your advert that you are an exotic dancer. I know most exotic dances, such as the Rumba, Samba and Tango. Perhaps we could dance together some day.

Before I forget, you mention one of your hobbies as going to the cinema. I am also interested in films. I adore Doris Day.

I do hope that you find time to write.
Yours sincerely

Johnny Urquhart

Chapter Forty-Five

John was a corporal for exactly seventeen days. On the 10th of January 1959 he was marched in front of the Station Commander. He was charged with being an instigator in a riot in the Airmen's Mess on Christmas Day. The charge sheet detailed that when the officers placed the Christmas turkey meals in front of the airmen two airmen stood on the table. These two were quickly followed by the remaining one hundred and ninety-eight airmen.

Chanting 'We don't want your Christmas pud', the airmen advised the serving officers where to stick the pudding.

John was reduced to the rank of Senior Aircraftsman and was confined to camp for thirty days. Sandy was fined five pounds and was also confined to camp for thirty days. The remaining airmen were not charged, as it was clearly impractical to charge every airman on the camp.

On 4th March 1959 John was officially presented with his 'no nookie' tie. This was presented to all airmen who had served twelve months on the station without the benefit of female relief. John pointed out that he actually qualified for twenty ties.

In May 1959, John, Sandy and six of their colleagues borrowed (officially) the service coach which was normally used to convey passengers to and from aircraft. Their destination was the Idris Palace Hotel in Cyreniaca. The official reason for the travel, and the only reason that the coach request was granted, was that it was an educational trip to see the ancient ruins at Derna.

The coach left El Adem in the early hours of the morning, on its two hundred mile journey. Included in the emergency rations was twenty crates of Amstel beer. There was also twenty four water bottles. They were taking no chances on the possibility of dehydration. None of them were taking the risk of being stuck in the desert with John, singing religious songs until being rescued.

In the true tradition of anything John was involved with organising, they arrived at the hotel to find that the hotel had a strict 'no alcohol' policy.

The 'no alcohol' policy was quickly resolved, by using the towing rope from the coach, to hoist the Amstel crates onto the first floor balcony, and from there to one of the bedrooms.

The hotel was first class. None of the airmen had ever experienced such luxury. John and Sandy shared a twin room. For the first time in over a year John had the use of a proper shower and the comfort of a bed without a straw mattress.

The eight airmen sat down to dinner that evening. They had difficulty concentrating on the meal as several of the residents of the hotel were young and, more importantly, female. The girls were escorted by clearly very rich Arabs, and bodyguards. There being no prospect in the female direction the boys returned to the bedrooms after dinner and drank. After drinking most of the Amstel, they returned to the hotel lounge.

They were asked to leave the hotel at midnight following an incident involving John and one of the escorted young ladies. The lecherous look on John's face had been enough to convince the girl's minders that John was not after the girl's autograph.

Events came to a head however when one of the hotel's security staff discovered the tow rope leading up to the first floor balcony. Suspecting that there may be thieves at work the security guard checked some of the bedrooms. He found clear evidence of an illegal drinks party under way.

The coach left the hotel on its return journey to El Adem at eight o'clock that morning. The airmen had to sleep in the coach for six hours, waiting for one of them to sober up sufficiently enough to drive.

They never did see the ruins at Derna.

Chapter Forty-Six

The twin Canberra jets stood side by side on the runway at El Adem. John was strapped into the navigator's position in one aircraft. Across fifty feet of tarmac, Sandy waved from his navigator's position in the other aircraft. The intrepid duo were on their way to Malta.

The visit to Malta had been arranged by the squadron commander of 9 Squadron. The squadron was based in Malta, but used the El Adem bombing range for target practice. The gesture was in appreciation of the efforts made by the Air Traffic Control and Movements staff at El Adem, in assisting in the operation of the Canberra Squadron.

Only two seats were up for grabs. Twenty names went into the hat. The first name drawn was one of the air traffic controllers. Sandy was drawn next, followed by John as reserve. John was used to being a reserve. He had enough experience in The Boys Brigade. But on this occasion he desperately wanted to take part in the game. He had heard stories about the night life in Malta.

The day before the flight the air traffic controller withdrew from the trip. It had cost John and Sandy three months supply of customs-seized free cigarettes to convince the air traffic clerk that he did not want to go to Malta. The cigarettes were not enough. It took the address of Jessica, the Clydeside exotic dancer, to sway the decision.

In May 1959, dressed in a flying suit, John put on an aircrew helmet. He actually felt that he was in the Royal Air Force. His civilian clothes, the ones that he was wearing when he first landed at El Adem, were stowed in the empty bomb bay.

The Canberras were cleared for take-off. Within a few minutes they were over the practice bombing range. There were no bombs to be dropped. This was just a familiarisation exercise for the navigator, who was in the position normally taken by the bomb-aimer. Sandy and John occupied the navigator's seat in their respective Canberra.

John's Canberra swooped over the range several times. Down it dived heading for the earth, before checking and swooping up into the heavens. John lost count of the number of times the aircraft dived and swooped. He had a feeling of déjà-vu.

He was thirty minutes into the flight, still swooping up and down over the bombing range, before the reason for the déjà-vu dawned on him.

The Beverley flight at trade training.

But this time he had no sick bag.

The call of "Abort, Abort, Urquhart's being sick," came over John's headset.

Forty minutes later both aircraft touched down in Malta. By this time John was wishing he had never seen a Canberra. The crew were wishing they had never seen John.

"Are you normally sick on aircraft?" the pilot of John's aircraft asked.

John thought of his four flights to-date. Aircraft on fire twenty-five per cent. Aircraft with engine trouble twenty five per cent. Aircraft on which he was sick fifty per cent.

"Not normally," he replied, cursing the exuberance of

the night before, when he and Sandy had sat drinking into the early hours, contemplating the excitement of the following three days.

Having received his by now customary rollicking, John, accompanied by Sandy, set off for the flesh-pots of Malta. They started off with the Salvation Army hostel. Not with any thoughts of fulfilling erotic fantasies. The Sally Ann was to be their base. Here they would eat and sleep, whilst recovering from what they fully expected to be a weekend to remember.

Booking into the Sally Ann brought John down to earth. The girl behind the reception desk was stunning. He had never seen a Maltese girl before, but John was convinced that women could not get any lovelier.

"You're beautiful," John said, drooling.

The girl looked at John. The signs of his air sickness were still evident.

She turned away in disgust.

John's first encounter with a girl in over fifteen months was a disaster.

Following ablutions, John and Sandy proceeded to Valletta, the capital of Malta. This, they had been advised, was 'the place' for a good time. Neither John nor Sandy had ever experienced a good time, so they had no idea what to expect.

They entered Strait Street. 'The Gut', as it was better known to British servicemen, was a long street with bars on either side. There appeared to be over fifty drinking dens on each side of the road. If the Lads from the Ferry were looking for adventure, there was a reasonable chance of finding it here.

Their visit to 'The Gut' lasted forty-five minutes.

The first bar they entered, laughingly named 'The Egyptian Queen', was unprepossessing in its external appearance. But the outside was a palace compared to the inside.

John thought he was in a nightmare. He was reminded of the horror films at the La-Scala cinema. He looked around the room. He was in a clone factory producing Mary Wilson's mother. Acres of hennaed hair blanked out the area of the bar, whilst dozens of crimson coloured hands groped in the air, seeking to touch the boys' bodies.

Cries of "Want a good time," and "Come here big boy," floated across the room from every corner. One old crone, supported by a walking stick, blew a kiss at John.

Not for the first time in their lives, the boys fled.

As the boys ran out the door, a group of sailors entered. Two seconds later, John heard a scream from one of the sailors. The scream ended abruptly.

Entering two further dens of iniquity was enough to convince the boys that they had not been in the desert long enough. Sandy summed it up by saying that he would need to have been at El Adem for forty years and have gone blind, before he could entertain the thought of being touched by 'the harlots from hell'.

Luck, however, was with the by now very dejected, adventurers. Well, for a short time. The boys found a coffee bar and spent a few hours listening to the juke-box and eating and drinking. The waitresses were pretty and pleasant. The boys had found their niche.

But the evening dragged on. At midnight the coffee-bar closed. After exchanging addresses with several of the waitresses, with promises to write, John and Sandy headed back to the Sally Ann.

To find it closed.

They began to look for alternative accommodation. They eventually found a hotel just off Strait Street, back in 'The Gut' area. The hotel looked rough. It certainly did not live up to its name 'Rest in Heaven'. John and Sandy entered. They were advised that beds were available. At a rate of two shillings and sixpence each, the boys could have a bed for the night in a shared dormitory, sectioned off into one-man cubicles.

The sound of snoring in the 'Rest in Heaven' stifled the outside sounds of drunken servicemen being ejected from the pubs in Strait Street, and the heated arguments between Army and Navy inebriates. But the Navy was not needed there. The Army would have been perfectly content fighting among themselves.

It was like The Meeting Rooms in Inverness on a Saturday night.

John had been sleeping only fifteen minutes when he was shaken awake. A male voice said, "Can I share with you mate?"

John opened his eyes. There was a man, a giant of a man, covered in tattoos, sitting on John's bed. The man was naked.

It took the naked visitor five minutes, speaking quietly, and using sign language, to get through to John what his wishes were.

John did not run this time. He screamed.

"Sandy, I've got a poof sitting on my bed."

Strange sounds throughout the dormitory ceased. Two naked men, clutching sailor hats, ran out of two cubicles, back into their own cubicles.

A short while later the boys were at the 'The British Hotel'. A large Union Flag hung outside.

"This looks better," Sandy commented.

It was better than the 'Rest in Heaven'. But it was five shillings each, for a bed in a twin room. John pointed out that it was three o'clock in the morning, and the rate for the whole night should not apply. A shrug from the old man manning the reception desk indicated that he could not have cared less what the time was. The rate was five shillings. However, if the boys were prepared not to sign the guest register, and share in a room for four, he would settle for three shillings each.

The boys agreed. The old man pocketed the money.

As luck would have it, the beds allocated to John and Sandy were nearest the door of the four man room. The luck was required when a very drunken Scottish voice, speaking from the end bed exclaimed, "That's the two perverts who got us thrown out of The Meeting Rooms in Inverness."

John looked at Sandy. Sandy looked at John. They were on the verge of pointing out that they had never been to Inverness, when John noticed the Gordon Highlander kilts lying at the end of the beds of the other room occupants.

Using the training gained from being deputy commander of the Laurel Avenue gang, coupled with several experiences since then, Sandy shouted, "Run."

They were on their way back to the Sally Ann, resigned to spend the remainder of the night on the pavement when Sandy remarked. "We've had more bloody running practice than Roger Bannister."

Chapter Forty-Seven

Having been admitted into the Sally Ann at daybreak, the boys arose after four hours sleep, determined not to waste a moment of the break. One day had already been taken up, and they were no nearer doing what they had come to Malta to do. The word girlfriend no longer applied. They just wanted a girl. They were both twenty-one years old and although John and Alison appeared to be engaged, they had not even kissed, excluding the 'kiss of life' incident on the first night John met Alison. Sandy had not even been that successful.

John and Sandy spent the remainder of the day sight-seeing. Malta was still suffering the effects of the Great Siege during the Second World War when the island had been awarded the George Cross. The island was nowhere near as bomb-damaged as Tobruk, but signs of damage were still there.

They returned to the coffee-bar where they had spent most of the previous evening. The waitresses made them very welcome. One even provided John with a photograph of herself, and asked him to write to her.

On leaving the coffee bar the boys decided to head away from 'The Gut' district, home of Count Dracula's daughters.

It was Sandy who saw the sign. 'Rosies Bar – Exotic Dancers'. Red light bulbs festooned around the door. The place had an air of depravity.

The boys entered. To their surprise it was quite a

classy place compared to The Egyptian Queen. At least there was no blood on the floor, and the hostesses had normal coloured hair.

They were drinking their third Hop Leaf beer when two girls, wearing scantily clad costumes, walked onto a small stage. A red spotlight shone on the girls as they danced together. John and Sandy were mesmerised. This was what they had come to Malta to see. But at two shillings for a bottle of beer, three drinks was all they could afford. Their resources were limited. John had spent most of his money on arrival at the airport, when he had to pay for a new aircrew headset, and for the Canberra cockpit to be cleaned.

John was on a high. So this was exotic dancing. This was what Jessica his Glasgow girlfriend did. He almost willed himself back to El Adem, so that he could write to her.

Next door to 'Rosies Bar' was 'The Prince Albert'. The boys were debating on whether or not to enter this bar when their minds were made up for them. A group of Royal Navy ratings entering the bar advised the lads that it was the best bar in Malta.

And so it turned out.

John and Sandy had never met a friendlier crowd. The sailors were all from the aircraft carrier H.M.S. Eagle, which was anchored just outside the Grand Harbour.

The invitation, and acceptance, all happened in a matter of moments. One moment John was saying that he and Sandy had to get back to the Sally Ann as it closed at midnight. The next moment they were being invited to go back to the ship with the sailors, on the grounds that there were Wrens on board, and the Wrens 'had a thing' for R.A.F. types.

John and Sandy were due to fly back the following

afternoon. This was their last opportunity to live it up, before going back to the desert.

They took the bait.

The only boat that either of the boys had been on before had been the ferry boat to the Black Isle. The duty crew boat which took them from the quay at Valletta to the Eagle, could not be compared to the slow plod of the Eilean Dubh. But John and Sandy were beyond the point of no return. This was their adventure. Here they where, the Lads From The Ferry, speeding across the Grand Harbour, Malta, to board the largest ship in the Royal Navy.

The boys wore civilian clothes. This, they were assured by a Leading Seaman, would allow them to board ship without being asked for identity cards. The duty watch would assume that they were Royal Navy Petty Officers.

The assurance was sound. After clambering out of the small launch and climbing up a rope ladder, which swayed in the night-time breeze, the boys were on board the ship.

The instruction they were given was simple. Follow the Leading Seaman. He would take them straight to the Wrens quarters.

"Don't follow me all the way. When I give a hand signal go down the hatch to my left." This was the instruction from the Leading Seaman.

After they had walked what seemed to John and Sandy to be about two miles, the Leading Seaman shot out his left hand. Sandy and John scuttled down a hatch, heading for the bowels of the ship. They stopped after a few minutes, and decided to wait. Their waiting area was equipped with hammocks. Empty hammocks.

An hour later, having seen no sign of any life, let alone willing Wrens, Sandy stated the obvious.

"I think we've been set up."

John nodded disconsolately.

One hour later, after trying to get some sleep in a hammock and falling out three times, Sandy began to panic.

"I think we could be in big trouble. We've just managed to get on board the biggest ship in the Royal Navy by pretending to be Royal Navy Petty Officers. How the hell do we get off it?"

It was obvious from the look on John's face that the question was superfluous.

"Right, let's go back on deck," decided Sandy. "We will worry about how we get back to dry land when we see the duty watch."

The boys attempted to retrace their way back to the deck, but got completely lost. At one stage they found themselves in a weapons storage area. Signs in the entrance to the area advised 'Out of bounds. Engineer Officer. Weapons and Electric's only'.

They realised that they were in potentially serious trouble. They were in the secure weapons area of a Royal Navy ship. If caught there, the repercussions would go beyond a thirty day confinement to camp, which, at El Adem, meant thirty days drinking in the N.A.A.F.I. They were looking at a sentence in a military detention centre.

They encountered the deck quite unexpectedly. But, once on deck, they had no idea where they were in relation to the duty watch station they had passed on boarding ship. They walked for ten minutes, without seeing a soul. Then Sandy realised that they were close to the point where they had joined the ship.

He advised John.

John stopped.

The boys conferred.

A few minutes later, as confident as could be, they strode up to the guard on duty watch. A young able seaman was sitting at a small table, reading a copy of 'Health and Efficiency Magazine'. John momentarily felt very homesick, thinking of his brother James.

"Leave the talking to me," John said to Sandy.

John strode up to the watch table, with Sandy trailing him. The young sailor looked up and, on seeing John, jumped to his feet and saluted.

"Sir, can I help you?" the duty watch asked.

John drew himself up and stated. "We wish to get back to Grand Harbour on a matter of urgency. We have to connect with a flight to our ship which is docked in Libya."

"Certainly Sir, I shall call out the Watch-Keeper." Saying this, the sailor pressed a button on his desk.

John picked up the copy of 'Health and Efficiency' and looked at the young sailor.

"I hope you don't make a habit of reading on duty. I intend to confiscate this." Saying this John rolled up the magazine and put it in his pocket.

Two minutes later the Watch-Keeper had spoken to John and Sandy. On hearing their story he called out the duty watch to take the lads back to Grand Harbour. The duty crew assembled on deck, and began to prepare the launch for its return to harbour.

In charge of the duty crew was the Leading Seaman who had invited John and Sandy on board ship. He pulled out a ships log.

"For the record gentlemen, could you please sign the duty watch call out book?" he requested.

Without hesitation, John picked up the proffered pen, and wrote 'Sub Lt L Costello'.

Sandy wrote 'Sub Lt. O. Hardy' directly beneath

John's name and added, 'H.M.S. Camel, Tobruk Docks'.

This was the moment of truth. Would the duty Watch-Keeper check the book and ask for their official identification. It would not have mattered. Neither of the lads had identification with them.

But no request was made.

On leaving the watch boat at the dockside, John apologised to the Leading Seaman for getting him out of bed. He returned the Leading Seaman's salute, taking care not to drop the bundle he had picked up from the Watch Boat.

At five o'clock that morning John and Sandy arrived back at the Sally Ann. They were relieved, exhausted, but exhilarated.

The Canberras returned to El Adem that afternoon. On this occasion there was no practice bombing run. John was handed a sick bag as he strapped himself into the aircraft. The Flying Officer in the pilot's seat looked at John.

"So, you're Urquhart are you. You do realise that you've disrupted the whole of our training schedule?"

In the N.A.A.F.I. that evening John and Sandy held court with twenty of their fellow airmen as they recounted their exploits and successes with the girls of Malta. Their stories bore no relation to the truth. At one stage in the elaborations, John produced a photograph of the waitress in the coffee bar, the one, according to John, with whom he had the night of his life.

The photograph hit the table.

Like a hand of poker, four identical photographs landed on top of it.

They had no need to embroider the H.M.S. Eagle incident. It became public knowledge within twenty-four hours of their arrival back at El Adem.

John was handed a copy of a signal. The signal read:–

From Flt Lt A Pratt, Officer in Charge of Accounting R.A.F. El Adem.

To Officer in Charge of Accounting H.M.S. Eagle.

DTG:– 250559. 0815 hours Zulu.

Subject:– Ships of the Desert

Contents:– I am at a loss to understand why you should be asking an R.A.F. station in the Libyan Desert to reimburse you for the cost of your duty watch being called out, and for a replacement White Ensign. We have no Royal Navy secondment here and have never heard of the officers in question. Has it not dawned on you that Costello and Hardy may just be a couple of comedians.

Get a grip.

Signal Ends.

On the same day that the signal was sent, John and Sandy were marched in front of the Station Commander.

"I'd lay a month's wages that you two are behind this dispute with the Navy. I should take the matter further but it could be embarrassing. Off the record we're all delighted that someone's shown the Navy up for the nincompoops they are. But if either of you step out of line once more you'll end up inside," the Station Commander stated.

The lads threw their hats in the air when they were safely outside the Station Commander's office.

The following evening a White Ensign flew above the El Adem N.A.A.F.I. John had picked up the flag when he had disembarked from the Watch Boat taking him back to Grand Harbour. The Leading Seaman realised what John was doing, but made no comment. As the instigator of John and Sandy being on board H.M.S. Eagle in the first place, he was in no position to challenge them.

A few days later John was handed a copy of yet another signal.

From:– Commander in Chief, Mediterranean Fleet.
To:– Air Officer Commanding Near East Air Force
DTG 310559 1020 hrs Zulu
Subject:– Theft of White Ensign
1.   Please take all possible steps to identify culprits in theft of White Ensign from H.M.S. Eagle.
1.   This matter is extremely serious and is a slur on the Royal Navy.
2.   The culprits had identified themselves as Sub Lt. Costello and Sub Lt. Hardy. It is thought that they may be airmen, possibly based in North Africa.
3.   This matter is now in the hands of the Provost Marshall, with the intention of Court Martial proceedings being taken.
4.   The signal from your Officer in Charge Accounting Services El Adem to Officer in Charge Accounting Services H.M.S. Eagle is not helpful. We are not a bunch of comedians in the Royal Navy.

Commander R Jones, Royal Navy
Signal Ends.

A rash of signals followed between the R.A.F. stations and Army garrisons in the Near East in an effort to track down the culprits. One of the signals, from the R.A.F. officer in charge of administration at the Tobruk Garrison, reminded the A.O.C. that a company of Gordon Highlanders had been on desert training in the El Adem area during the period under investigation. It was possible, he suggested, that some of the Highlanders had been in transit in Malta at the time of the incident.

Chapter Forty-Eight

802 S.A.C. Urquhart,
Air Movements Section,
R.A.F. El Adem,
B.F.P.O. 56

Miss Jessica Rawlings,
The Ship Inn,
Dock Road,
Clydeside,
Glasgow.

20 May 1959

My Dear Jessica,

Thank you for your letter. You must be extremely busy as this is only the third time you have written in four months. Thank you also for the photograph of yourself. Has anybody ever told you that you look just like Doris Day?

I have just come back from Malta. A most exciting experience. I cannot begin to tell you some of the things that I got up to. Some secrets are best kept!!!!

The most exciting thing is that I have found out what an exotic dancer is. It really is interesting. Do you use snakes in your act? Do you wear many clothes?

I am quite excited at the thought of seeing you. I cannot think of anything that would get me as excited as watching you perform.

As you can see I am no longer a Corporal. It appears that the Records Office Clerk in Station Headquarters got things mixed up. I am back to being a Senior Aircraftsman, which is just about one spot more important than a dustman. I'm sorry if I sound petulant. I'm just so bored with the same monotonous routine. It is humping freight all day and drinking all evening.

If all that wasn't bad enough, I also have to put up with the same gramophone records every day. I loathe the sound of Beethoven.

I don't think I mentioned it but I was born in Inverness. I don't know if you know the town. I was born in South Drive, but now live in Dalneigh. If you ever go to Inverness I would love to show you around. There is a bar there, The Harbour Inn. You might like it.

I have passed your name onto one of our Air Traffic Controllers. I am sure he will write soon. I enclose ten pounds for your Save The Animals fund, and ten pounds so that you can visit your sick grandmother.

Can't wait till I see your routine. They don't call me 'Big Boy' for nothing.

Love,

Johnny.

P.S. By the way my name is Johnny, not Tommy. It must be my bad handwriting.

Chapter Forty-Nine

S.A.C. J. Urquhart,
Air Movements Squadron,
B.F.P.O.56

Miss Alison Forbes,
Hill House,
Up the Hill,
Inverness.

20 May 1959

My Dearest Darling Alison,

I miss you so much even though I have been very busy. My job is very demanding with having to make decisions all the time.

I had a most interesting time at a Roman ruins in a country in the Middle East. That is as much as I can say about it. Security.

I followed this up with a few days assessing the bomb damage in a major Middle East location. The information will be used to see if a new airfield can be built.

I must get off this subject of work, as I can see I may say the wrong thing, and get us both in serious trouble with the authorities.

It is so good to hear that your grandmother is recovering and getting her memory back. As you have repeatedly said, that Ferry place is enough to put anybody in a state of shock.

Time is so short and I am so busy that I barely have time to write letters. As I cannot say too much about my secret work, it is difficult to know what to write about.

Perhaps we could see a ballet performance when I get home. I quite like the idea of watching elegant dancers.

Must rush, darling, you are the only girl in the world for me.

Your loving fiancé (I still cannot believe how lucky I am),

John.

XXXXX

Chapter Fifty

802 S.A.C. Urquhart,
Air Movements Section,
R.A.F. El Adem,
B.F.P.O.56

Miss Alison Forbes,
Hill House,
Up the Hill,
Inverness.

28 May 1959

Dear Alison,

I have received your letter dated the 24th of this month.

I assume there is no point in my trying to explain that it was a genuine error that I put the letter to Jessica, my friend in Glasgow, in your envelope by mistake. Thank you for posting it to her.

I am sorry that you have adopted the tone that you have. I still think my job is quite important, and it is not my fault that I was born down the Ferry

I think it was churlish of you to throw your Bravingtons engagement ring into the river. I may have been able to get back the five pounds I paid for it.

Tell your grandmother she is right. I was born on Christmas Day 1938. Although how she would know that is beyond me. She clearly has all her faculties back. She must have known my mother. Perhaps they went to the same school?

I await the letter from your solicitor.

Yours (or not as it happens) sincerely,

Johnny (yes Johnny) Urquhart.

Chapter Fifty-One

Marie Winngate looked around her apartment which was located on the smart west side of Glasgow. She had done well for herself. Only twenty-one and already she owned the apartment, and had a share in a pub in Clydeside.

She had collected her mail from 'The Ship' only that morning, and was now scanning through the letters, removing all the cash, before she read the letters later in the day.

It was late evening before she got the opportunity to read the letters. She had been busy that day. The idea of starting a massage parlour intrigued her, particularly with the young girl Norma Wallace fronting the organisation. She had heard Norma was from Inverness. Norma was only fifteen, but she had been modelling for a year, thanks to the initiative of a neighbour, who had introduced her to the profession by sending her a magazine.

Marie began to read the letters. You never know, there might just be another mug, just ready to be convinced of her needs for her sick mother, dying aunt, or any other money making scheme she could think of.

The letters were all addressed to Jessica Rawlings. The name she had assumed five years before, when she had found that using her own name was making life difficult with the police

It was the letter from the wimp at R.A.F. El Adem that caught her eye. The letter, and cash, had been forwarded by an Alison Forbes from Inverness, with a nasty covering letter. The twenty pounds was good news. The bad news was that she knew Johnny Urquhart. For four months she had been writing to Tommy Urquhart. The name had meant nothing. But Johnny, combined with The Ferry, meant a great deal.

Jessica decided that she would write to John for the last time, saying that she could no longer write to him as she was marrying a vicar. She felt a tinge of regret. Johnny would have been worth at least another fifty quid over the next year.

She continued looking through her mail. Four of the naval ratings had said they fancied Sophia Loren, whilst one of the older seamen had a crush on Veronica Lake.

Marie, alias Jessica, looked at the photographs of Sophia and Veronica that she had cut out of the Film Preview Magazine. A bit of touching up and they would be perfect to send out in the next letters to the servicemen stating that it was a photograph of herself. She was still unsure what to do about the R.A.F. Flight Lieutenant who said that he liked Rock Hudson.

She threw away the letter to Alison that Johnny had sent her by mistake. But it gave her a good in-sight into John's mentality, which, she thought, may just prove useful one day.

Chapter Fifty-Two

Four days after receiving his 'Dear John' letter from Alison, John held his 'Dear John' celebrations in the N.A.A.F.I.

It must have been the start of a long hot summer in the UK as three of John's fellow airmen had also received a 'Dear John' that week. The girls back in the UK were clearly getting restless.

The evening started off in traditional fashion with all the attendees, suitably refreshed, community singing "I've Never Felt More Like Singing The Blues." Due to the high volume of 'Dear Johns' received (one a month was the norm), there was maximum attendance, as colleagues rushed to either sympathise, or take the mickey out of, the rejected airmen.

John took pride of place. He was one of the very few ever to have received a 'Dear John, Dear John' letter.

He was provided with three dartboards, one for Alison, one for the waitress from Malta, and one for Jessica. He had decided, on receipt of Alison's letter, that in future he would be a one woman guy.

Each dart that hit Alison's photograph was greeted with roars of applause. Her disfigurement was insignificant however, compared to the damage meted out on the waitress. Five frustrated airmen, John included, launched a volley of darts at the young girl, who was probably in much the same position as the airmen were. All she wanted was a boyfriend.

Jessica suffered a more fortunate fate. Only one dart had hit her face before an eager fan, due to be repatriated to Glasgow the following month, rushed up and saved her. "Just in case I get a 'Dear John' from my wife in the next few weeks," he explained.

Once John had completed his task of obliterating Alison, the other 'Dear John' recipients pinned their photographs to the dartboards. Three dartboards, three fresh photographs.

On completion of the 'Dear John' ritual a large tub was placed in the middle of the room and the airmen lined up for a lucky dip. The tub contained over three hundred letters from hopeful pen-friends. The letters were in response to an advertisement placed in 'Lonely Hearts Magazine'.

The advertisement read:–

'Women wanted for lonely airmen who have been in the desert for two years. Any religion. Any age. Any size. Genuine respondents only. Write to S.A.C. Evans, Air Movements, R.A.F. El Adem, B.F.P.O.56'.

The fun did not stop at the 'Dear Johns' or the Lucky Dip. This was a special night. Air Traffic Control had been advised, in secret, that the Prime Minister's aircraft was due to fly above the airfield en route to a Middle East conference. The fly-over, at eight thousand feet, was expected at 2200 hours.

At 2159 hours, as the drone of an aircraft was heard high above the desert, John and Sandy stood outside the N.A.A.F.I., and dropping their trousers, raised their bare buttocks to the overhead Prime Minister.

In the Officers Mess, overlooking the N.A.A.F.I., Flight Lieutenant Smythe could not believe his eyes. He had not had as much excitement since playing hockey at Eton, when the boys had all shared a communal bath after the game.

Once the frustrations of the 'Dear Johns' had been exhausted, and the engine noise of the V.I.P aircraft had faded, all present proceeded to have a convivial evening. There was a record number of inmates in the guard-room that night.

John crawled back to his tent, crying his eyes out. He was now on his own. The love of his life, Alison, no longer existed.

He would never trust a woman again.

Five minutes later he was writing to Lesley, telling her how much he loved her.

Chapter Fifty-Three

Nurse Lesley Graham.
Nurses Home,
Royal Northern Infirmary,
Inverness.

2 June 1959

My Dearest Lesley,

Let me start by saying just how much I miss you. I know that sounds silly. I know that you only saw me briefly at the Nurses Dance. I know that we have only been writing to each other for a few months, but I have a soft spot for you. I do feel that there is something intimate between us. Let me know if you feel the same.

I have been surprisingly busy since I last wrote to you. I can understand why you were unable to respond straight away to my last letter. It must be difficult having to work in Inverness, and having to look after a sick mother on the Isle of Skye. Still, it sounds as though the hospital are very good to you, in giving you leave when required.

It is hard to believe that we have written over twenty letters to each other. I keep them in my bedside locker and read them over and over again.

Sandy and I had an exciting time in Malta. I'll tell you more about it when we meet.

We even managed to get on board H.M.S. Eagle, the Royal Navy aircraft carrier. To be quite honest, we should not have been there. But I will tell you all about that when I get home.

The girls in Malta are pretty, but not as nice as the girls in Inverness, and certainly not as beautiful as you. I thought the group photograph of the nurses dance was lovely. May I please have one of just you, I had difficulty picking you out in the group photograph.

Well, I'm chattering on here. Oh! Before I forget. The Prime Minister flew overhead a couple of days ago. You won't believe what Sandy and I did when his plane passed over. I'll tell you when I see you.

All my love,
Yours,

Johnny.
XXX

Chapter Fifty-Four

802 S.A.C. Urquhart
Air Movements Section,
R.A.F. El Adem,
B.F.P.O. 56

Mr J. Urquhart,
343 Laurel Avenue,
Inverness

10 June 1959.

Dear Dad,

Did you ever get to the stage in Burma when you wondered what it was all about. I feel the same here. This place is so depressing. I miss home desperately. I can see some sense in you having been in Burma as you had a war going on. Out here there is nothing happening. It feels like a waste of my life.

I'm sorry Dad. Here I go, moaning yet again. There is some fun. Sandy and I get up to some pranks, but these account for just a fraction of the time I have spent out here. Fifteen months. I'll never complain about Inverness being boring again.

I suspect what is depressing me is that I have finished with Alison. We were just not compatible. I have also stopped writing to the girl in Glasgow.

There is a strong probability that I will get my

Corporal stripes back. I don't know how these Record Clerks manage to get their records wrong. The Records Clerk at El Adem seems to have it in for me. I cannot think what I have done to upset him.

Tell James that I have another book for him. I will not send it through the post this time. It is good to know that Mr and Mrs Wallace are back together again, even though he has to attend Alcoholics Anonymous. I am sure that Norma will be very successful as a model, although I do think that fifteen is a bit young to do topless modelling. I cannot imagine her working in Glasgow.

At long last I managed to get on the trip to Malta. Sandy and I, through the luck of the draw, Ferry Style, were fortunate enough to fly in Canberra bombers. I wish I could have taken a photograph for you. I was dressed in a flying suit with a flying helmet, and was in radio contact with the pilot and navigator. I am sure Mum would have been proud of me.

Malta was great fun. We ended up on the navy ship H.M.S. Eagle, which took part in the last war.

Well Dad, there is not much else to say.

This makes my fortieth letter to you.

I miss the family. I cannot believe that I shall never see Mum again. I miss her so much.

Your loving son,

John

Chapter Fifty-Five

The Air Officer Commanding Middle East Air Force slowly opened his eyes. It felt as though something was drilling into his head. He remembered that the previous night he had been in the Officers Mess at R.A.F. Nicosia in Cyprus. He had just completed his annual inspection of the base. His next scheduled inspection was at R.A.F. El Adem in the Libyan Desert. He winced at the thought of going to that God forsaken hole.

The A.O.C. stretched out his hand. He felt something soft lying next to him. Jumping out of bed, hands shaking, he switched on the bedside lamp.

"Oh my God," he exclaimed, "who the hell are you?"

Flight Lieutenant Robson-Stuart raised himself up on one elbow. He was wearing pyjamas, emblazoned all over with tiny Rupert Bear motifs, which he had specially tailored in Singapore.

"Don't you remember?" he asked the A.O.C. "We met in the Officers Mess last night. I am the navigator on your tour."

The A.O.C. suddenly realised that he was stark naked, and that a complete nutter, dressed in Rupert Bear pyjamas was lying in his bed. The A.O.C. stopped himself from ringing the bell which would summon his batman. He already had a relationship with his batman. He did not want to make the situation any more difficult.

"You were absolutely wonderful last night," the rampant navigator continued, gazing at the A.O.C.'s body as he spoke.

Realisation flooded back to the A.O.C. Not just about the drink and the previous night, but about his whole tour of inspection. He was the one who had insisted that he should have a Beverley aircraft, in order that he could take his own staff-car, his Portaloo, additional supplies of toilet paper, and four crates of Gin.

He had been stuck in one of the desert airfields before when toilet paper and Gin supplies had run out. He was not taking any chances.

Apart from the hassle of the compulsory tour of inspection, he was still trying to resolve the crisis that had erupted over the theft of a White Ensign from the Royal Navy aircraft carrier H.M.S. Eagle. Investigators from all three services were scouring troop movement instructions, to establish precisely which servicemen had been on the island of Malta when the incident had occurred. The only lists that had not been checked, and which could not be checked for operational reasons, were those of the R.A.F. Canberra Squadrons on operational duties.

But things were moving in the A.O.C.'s favour. The Watch-Keeper on the Eagle had been certain that the two impostors were Scottish, and possibly Army. The Watch-Keeper had stated that he felt that the R.A.F. touch was just a ruse. The two servicemen on the duty launch were not bright enough to be in the Royal Air Force. To add to this information, the Army police had established that two privates in the Gordon Highlanders had been in Malta at the time, staying at The British Hotel, Valletta. More importantly, they had both been so drunk they could give no sensible account of their movements in the twenty-four hour period before, during, and after the White Ensign incident. One of them raved about a meeting room in Inverness, but nobody could make sense of his statement. The soldiers were adamant that two R.A.F. types had shared their room in the British Hotel. The hotel records showed otherwise. The old man on the reception desk was adamant that the only occupants of the hotel that night had been the two Gordon Highlanders. The old man had already invested his six shillings profit in Hop Leaf shares.

This did not solve the A.O.C.'s immediate problem, which was what to do with Flight Lieutenant Robson-Stuart. He looked at the Flight Lieutenant, who by this time was gazing mournfully into the eyes of the A.O.C.

"Oh, sod it," the A.O.C. muttered to himself, getting back into bed. "Let's see how many Rupert Bears we have here."

John and Sandy were on duty when the A.O.C.'s Beverley touched down at El Adem. This was good news. It meant that they were not taking part in the Guard of Honour Parade.

The rear freight doors of the Beverley were open, but no unloading ramps in place, when John encountered a problem with the restrainers holding down the A.O.C.'s car.

"Something does not look right, but I can't figure out what the problem is," he advised Sandy.

Sandy took a look at the restrainers. The webbing straps were wrapped across the car, and tied down on each side of the car. This ensured that the car would not move during flight. The car was sitting on rollers, to allow easy movement into and out of the aircraft.

"Let's take off all the webbing straps," suggested Sandy.

The webbing straps were removed, and John and Sandy looked at the car, which was now free of any restraints. John spotted the problem straight away. The rollers had not been fixed to the floor. The webbing straps had been holding the car, and the rollers, in place. But the rollers were face down on the floor. The Air Movers in Cyprus were clearly as thorough as John and Sandy.

It was at the precise moment of John spotting the lack of restrainers, and the upside down rollers, that the Sergeant Air Quartermaster for the flight decided to take a hand in the proceedings.

"We haven't got all bloody day," the Quartermaster stated. "Get this car off the aircraft so that the A.O.C. can use it." Saying this he got behind the car and pushed.

The car, and the rollers on which it was sitting, went the full length of the aircraft before falling out of the freight door, which was still without the benefit of the unloading ramps. There was an almighty crash as metal hit concrete.

Sandy looked at the Air Quartermaster, who had turned white.

"I don't suppose you noticed, Sergeant, but there were no restrainers on the rollers, and no unloading ramp." Sandy pointed out.

Airmen congregated at the rear of the aircraft to survey the damage. Not just to the car, but to the freight doors of the aircraft.

A voice in the crowd stated the obvious.

"Well, that's grounded the Beverley for a few days."

The amateur technical expert had just uttered these words, when the navigator for the flight, Flight Lieutenant Robson-Stuart, arrived at the rear of the aircraft.

Seasoned airmen, those who had been at El Adem long enough to remember previous incidents when the Flight Lieutenant had been stranded at El Adem, fled into the desert.

The Station Records Clerk, on hearing the news that Flight Lieutenant Robson-Stuart was stranded, rushed back to his tent to recover his cosmetics from his hiding place. Flight Lieutenant Smythe was on leave in Tripoli for a whole week. The Records Clerk could not believe his luck.

Chapter Fifty-Six

John could see that the woman was clearly a man, but
Sandy did not seem to care. The lads were in Bugis Street,
Singapore, heading, yet again, for another disappointment.

In October 1959, John and Sandy were transferred to a
movements team being used in the role of trouble-
shooters. Their duties, operating with the Mobile Air
Movements Team, was to accompany aircraft on
operational duties. This involved assisting the Air
Quartermaster in planning loads, travelling with the
aircraft, unloading at the destination, and then starting the
process all over again.

It took The Ferry Lads away from El Adem for a few
weeks.

If John thought El Adem was a hellhole, and it was,
his eyes were opened when he saw the R.A.F. bases at
Aden and Masirah Island.

Singapore was a paradise compared to the desert
airfields. John and Sandy stayed there for only three
weeks. But it was sufficient time to get them into trouble.

The encounter with the transvestite in Bugis Street
was to be expected. Most of the 'girls' operating in the bars
there were, in fact, boys.

John and Sandy spent three days checking out the
nightlife of Singapore. After their internment at El Adem,
it was a welcome relief.

'Out of Bounds to British Serviceman' signs were a
magnet to the Ferry Lads. Being pursued in rickshaws by

Navy Shore Patrol and Army Redcaps became part of the hourly routine.

It was in Changi Village, Singapore, that John was rescued by, ironically enough, one of the kilted regiments. The Queens Own Cameron Highlanders.

John had just finished his shift as part of his Mobile Air Movements duties, and was relaxing in Helen's Bar. The bar was actually a stall located in a side street in the village and was popular with British servicemen. It was not the most hygienic place in the world, but after a long shift a cool beer went down well.

He was on his third bottle of Tiger Beer when he was approached by a group of locals. All servicemen had been alerted to the fact that there was the possibility of local disturbances due to the political climate within the island.

The locals had taken exception to the way that John was leering after one of the young Chinese barmaids. They made their feelings quite clear when he was seized by four men, who systematically began to beat him. The first thing that went was John's glasses, which, in a way, helped. He did not want to know what they were doing to him.

Three minutes into the beating the Queens Own arrived on the scene. John had never been so relieved to see the British Army.

Having chased the local thugs away, the Highlanders looked at what they had rescued. It was a pitiful sight.

One of the soldiers began to empty the contents of John's pockets, on the basis that John owed them all a drink. Like Old Mother Hubbard's cupboard however, John's pockets were empty.

The Squaddies felt cheated. They had by this time realised that John was in the R.A.F. His Form 1250 was in his wallet. There was no love lost between the army and the Air Force.

John prepared himself for a further beating.

The soldier thumbing through John's wallet pulled out a piece of paper. It was a copy of the oath which had been signed by John and his four friends in the coffee bar in Inverness in 1955.

The soldier looked at John and then looked at the paper.

"I didn't recognise you without your glasses. How in Heavens name do you get yourself in so much trouble?" Alex Todd asked. "I don't suppose you've got married, and I can claim my five pounds?"

Chapter Fifty-Seven

802 Cpl. Urquhart,
Air Movements Section,
R.A.F. El Adem,
B.F.P.O.56

Mr J. Urquhart,
343 Laurel Avenue,
Inverness.

24 December 1959

Dear Dad,

Well, time is drawing on. Only another three months and I shall be out of here. If I survive that is. There is an air of intense despair about the place. What gives people in authority the right to put young men in a place like this for thirty months. Criminals are treated better.

All I seem to do lately when I write you is complain. I don't mean to. This place just drives me to it.

I suppose when I look on the positive side things aren't so bad. After all in the past year I have seen parts of North Africa, Malta, Singapore, Aden, and a few other places almost as bad as El Adem.

As you can see I finally got my Corporal stripes back.

I hear from Lesley almost daily now. I have a feeling that this could be the big one. She really does seem wonderful. I can't wait to meet her, I am so pleased that

James has forgiven me for the magazine incident. I wonder what his surprise is going to be.

I plan to have a big party when I return. But more than anything I just want to visit the Cummings Bar with you and James, to have my first drink in a pub with my Dad and my elder brother.

It's Christmas Eve. I expect this letter will leave here in about a week as there are no flights scheduled for the next few days.

By the time you get this the festivities will be over. I hope you had a lovely Christmas and a great Hogmanay. Love to all my brothers and sisters.

See you soon,

Fondest love from your son,

John

Chapter Fifty-Eight

802 Cpl. Urquhart,
Air Movements Section,
R.A.F. El Adem.
B.F.P.O.56

Nurse Lesley Graham,
Nurses Home,
Inverness.

24 December 1959

My Darling Lesley,

Christmas Eve – a time when lovers should be together. Oh, I know we're not lovers, (difficult to do that by post), but you know what I mean. I keep looking at your photograph, the one where you are wearing a ski outfit and snow goggles. You look so sporty.

As you can see I am a Corporal once again. Seems a bit pointless to me, as I have only a few weeks to go, (that sounds good).

I hope your mother recovers soon. It is nice that you will be having Christmas with her and your cousin. I was astonished to hear that your cousin was born in the Ferry part of Inverness. You must give me her name. I may have been in school with her.

Sandy is a bit frustrated at the moment. He has been writing to quite a lot of girls since he has been here, but they have all stopped writing to him. I dread to think what he has been saying in his letters. He does fantasize a bit.

Well I've seen quite a bit of the world since I left Inverness, but there's no place like home.

I hope you have received the Christmas present and card I sent. Singapore was excellent for shopping

The ring I sent you is just a gesture. Think of me when you wear it. Who knows what the future brings. We just don't know what life has in store for us.

All my fondest love,
From a lonely little airman,
Yours forever,

Johnny
XXXXX

Chapter Fifty-Nine

John was in the Airmen's Mess at El Adem, when he received the news of the death of his father. His father had died of a heart attack. John was devastated. He had not seen his father for nearly two years. He would never see him again.

A sand storm was raging as John received the news. The sand storm continued for four days, during which time there were no aircraft taking off, or landing, at El Adem.

John arrived back in Inverness two days after his father's funeral. He had been given ten days compassionate leave.

His brothers met him at the railway station. They embraced, clearly still shaken by the news. A few hours after arrival in Inverness, John visited Tomnahurich Cemetery. He laid some flowers on his parents' graves, and wept inconsolably.

On the second day of his homecoming John telephoned the Nurses' Home. He was advised that Nurse Graham was on compassionate leave for seven days due to ill-health in the family, but, knowing that John was in Inverness, would be at the Caley dance on the Saturday. John was due to return to El Adem on the Sunday morning.

To the tune of 'A White Sports Coat and a Pink Carnation' John dressed up for the dance at the Caley. Old habits died hard. His fourteen months of waiting to meet Lesley was over.

John was standing in the bar at the Caley with James, when he saw a group of people on the dance floor. Among them was the stunning girl he had seen at the Nurses Dance.

James turned to John, and looking at the group on the dance floor said, "I think it's time you met somebody who has been looking forward to seeing you."

John looked at the group again. The stunning girl was looking at him, smiling, beckoning him forward.

John, with his pint of beer in his hand, stepped away from the bar into the dance area. The first thing he noticed was that all the seating around the dance floor had been removed. The earlier complaints about lechers had obviously been taken seriously. The next thing he noticed was a sign stating 'No drinks in the dance-area'.

John was grabbed from behind.

"Can't you bloody read?" a voice screamed in his ear.

John was unceremoniously ejected from the Caley. He turned around and found himself looking at Billy Wilson, the same bouncer who had thrown him out of the Caley three years before. Mary Wilson's brother.

"Christ, don't you ever learn?" Billy mouthed through the glass doors.

The following day John left Inverness on his return to El Adem.

After fourteen months of writing to Lesley, he had still not spoken to her.

Chapter Sixty

The following eight weeks at El Adem were a drudge for John. His heart was not in anything. He wrote to Lesley every week, although the tone of their letters was very subdued. John attributed this to the death of his father and Lesley's own family health problems.

Two weeks before final departure from El Adem, the movement instructions came through for John and Sandy. They were to return to the UK on the same flight, and would be discharged together. John cheered up. He would see Lesley soon.

But it was not to be. A week before final departure from El Adem, John received a letter from Lesley. Lesley had returned to the Isle of Skye to care for a mother who was terminally ill. Lesley felt there was no future in their relationship. It was better to end it, and keep the memories. The matter was not up for discussion. The letter was brief, but emotional. Lesley and John were not meant to be together.

John was distraught. The beautiful girl he had seen at the Nurses Home and Caley would not be his.

He did not place the letter on the 'Dear John' dartboard. It meant too much to him.

Back at R.A.F. Cardington, John and Sandy received their final discharge papers. They were instructed to retain most of their uniform, as they would be on Reserve Service for the following five years.

The Lads from the Ferry boarded the train in London on its way to Inverness. They were finally on their way home.

They were outside Glasgow when they reached the decision. Get rid of their Air Force kit. Put the time in the desert behind them.

A shower of clothing descended on the tenements of Glasgow shortly after the train pulled out of the station. John thought back to his days of collecting coal on the Inverness to Dingwall railway track. He wondered what the Gorbals kids would make of all the clothing coming down from heaven.

Four hours later the lads were home. It was a Wednesday. The Caley dance was on.

But it was not the same. There was no Lesley. There was no girl John recognised.

Two weeks later the lads reached a decision. They were going to re-join the Royal Air Force. There was nothing to keep them in Inverness. They needed excitement.

They contacted the Recruiting Office in Inverness. They were informed that the Royal Air Force would be delighted to have them back. Provided they signed on for five years.

The boys signed. There were plenty of adventures awaiting them.

They reported to R.A.F. Cardington to be re-processed..

Thirty minutes after arriving at Cardington they were both on a charge of 'not being in possession of a full reserve uniform'. When asked where his kit was John replied, straight faced, "It's gone to help the poor in the Glasgow Branch of the Billy Wilson Foundation."

They were each fined ten pounds. The new uniforms

cost them an additional eighty-five pounds.

"It's good to be back" said Sandy.

"Let's see if that bird still works in the N.A.A.F.I." said John.

Chapter Sixty-One

The following announcement appeared in The Inverness Herald in March 1962.

KESSOCK PRIMARY SCHOOL
GRAND REUNION

Staff and Pupils who attended the school between 1943 and 1950 are invited to a Grand Reunion to be held at the school on Friday 23 April, 1962

Please contact the School Secretary for further details and formal invitations.

John and Sandy were stationed at R.A.F. Northolt, South London, at the time. The newspaper cutting was forwarded to John by his brother James. Neither of the lads had been back in Inverness since March 1960. It seemed an ideal time to return home, 'to check out the talent' as Sandy put it. Their score with the girls was still zero, despite the fact that both boys were now twenty-four. Sandy had briefly courted a secretary from Ruislip, but had terminated the relationship when she starting talking about children.

Meanwhile, in Glasgow, Marie Winngate was reading her copy of The Herald. She had been a regular subscriber for two years, having realised that there was a lucrative market in the town from the squaddies at the Cameron Barracks and the seamen docking at the harbour. She had already made enquiries about purchasing The Harbour Inn.

Chapter Sixty-Two

Probationary Police Constable David Thomson was on duty, eating his meat pie, when he spotted the latest flyer from headquarters. Despite the gravy dripping from his pie onto the paper, he could still make out the woman pictured in the 'wanted for questioning' column.

He read the information alongside the picture. The woman was wanted in connection with a series of frauds perpetrated against servicemen based overseas. Word had reached the Glasgow CID that she was switching operations, and could possibly be targeting servicemen based in the UK The details had been forwarded to the Highland Constabulary because of the army barracks in the town.

P.P.C. Thomson looked at the photograph again. He knew he had seen the woman. Her hair had been slightly different, but he was certain that he had seen her before.

It was two o'clock the following morning before it dawned on the constable where he had seen the woman before.

He put down the album of coloured stickers that he had gained at Sunday School. He had kept the stickers to remind him of Moira Ferguson, the vicar's daughter. Moira was much younger than the constable, but he had always hoped that one day she would turn to him. Moira had thought it strange when he had joined the Sunday School at the age of twenty-one. She put it down to the fact that he was just another nutter.

The Hill District. The bridge at the Ness Islands. Slowly it came back to him. Seven years ago.The toe-rag from the Ferry, Sandy Roberts. The girl he was with was the woman in the photograph. He now knew where Marie Winngate, alias Jessica Rawlings, alias Doris Turner, lived.

She lived at Hill House, Up The Hill.

Two minutes later the constable remembered where he had seen the toe-rag for the first time. It was at the 'Kessie School' sports day in 1947 when a police dog had been bitten. The lad was the chief suspect. He recalled the boy walking the girl Up The Hill. Yes, it was the same lad. The boy had not worn spectacles at the sports day. He had been about two feet smaller, and weighed about five stone less than the lad going Up The Hill, but P. P.C. Thomson had seen worse photo-fits.

But the name did not ring true. Sandy Roberts?

No.

The name of the dog biter was Urquhart, John Urquhart.

The constable was so excited that he did not realise that he was crushing his collection of Sunday School stickers.

A sting, he thought. Urquhart and Winngate work as a team, using aliases. This could be what he needed for his promotion to constable. He had been a probationary constable for eighteen years.

At four o'clock that morning the Hill District was awoken by the sounds of dogs barking and doors being broken down. The riot squad had arrived at Hill House.

Alison was arrested on charges of fraud and deception. Her grandmother passed out at the thought of her granddaughter going to prison. The comment from one of the neighbours was 'I always knew they were a bad lot, always in trouble with the police. They should live down the Ferry'.

Further charges were pressed against Alison, when she insisted that her name was Alison Forbes. This was added to her list of aliases. She was in even deeper trouble when she admitted that she knew John Urquhart. They did not believe her when she said that she had not seen him, or heard from him, for over two years.

Alison appeared at the Sheriffs Court the following day and was detained in custody pending further enquiries. A report on her case, and her photograph, appeared in The Herald the next day. The same day that Jocky Winngate bought The Herald to read the births, deaths and marriages columns, an old Inverness custom. Jocky liked to keep track of his large family.

On opening the newspaper Jocky was confronted with a picture of his daughter. He was not sure which one. But he had a feeling that his chickens were coming home to roost.

In the social column of the same edition of the newspaper, there was a reminder that the 'Kessock School' reunion was to be held that evening.

Chapter Sixty-Three

John and Sandy entered the school assembly hall together. They looked around. The hall was much smaller than John remembered. The noise of laughter and conversation filled the air.

"I hope they don't think we're here as partners," John commented.

"Right, let's mix," said John. "See who we know. I wonder if Slimey Jefferson will be here?"

"Do you mean Smiley Jefferson?" Sandy asked. "Don't you think it's about time that you stopped fantasizing about primary school. Those bloody daft ideas you had about Smiley, and the bit about the teachers carrying crosses and getting Commando training. Your brother didn't half fill your head with stupid thoughts."

"Oh, I know it was all in my mind," John replied. "But it was much more interesting than the boredom of just doing maths and history. You needed an imagination to survive in The Kessie."

Sandy wandered off and was soon in conversation with Violet MacDonald. Violet was accompanied by her boyfriend Billy Wilson. In the course of their discussion, Sandy learned that Violet's arsonist career had not come to an end after burning down the Dalneigh farmhouse, when she had played the part of an Indian squaw. She had later burnt down the church when she was rejected as a Sunday School teacher. Sandy couldn't figure out why Violet had been rejected. Half the town appeared to be Sunday School teachers.

Billy Wilson seemed friendly enough, passing the comment to Sandy, "I see you've got the weirdo with you."

John saw some of his old school pals scattered around the room. He recognised Irene Norman, Old Willie MacDonald's animal tormentor, chatting away to Tommy Brown, the machete kid. "God help us if those two plan to get together," he reflected.

Irene introduced John to Tommy Ross, who was chatting away to Jessie Williams and Betty Fraser. All disagreements about the three-legged race, and the Eilean Dubh near-drowning incident, appeared to have been forgotten.

John looked around the room. He spotted Miss Shaw, his old PE teacher. Wearing a wedding ring he noticed, but looking extremely attractive. He hoped there would be some dancing later on. He quite fancied Miss Shaw now, even though she was over forty.

Mrs Fraser, his old Religious Instruction teacher, was there, having been reinstated to her position several months after the egg incident which had started the riot at the school sports. She was speaking to Miss Goodall, who had recovered from her nervous breakdown. Miss Goodall, who was wearing a six-inch cross on a gold chain around her neck, went pale when she saw John enter the hall.

Mrs Fraser and Miss Goodall were over-heard remarking on how many of the children resembled each other, almost as though they had the same father.

A voice breathed into John's ear.

"Hello, big boy," the voice said. "Remember me?"

John turned, and found himself looking at Alison.

"Alison, what are you doing here?" he asked, "I had no idea you went to the 'Kessie'. I thought you detested everything about the Ferry area."

Marie Winngate looked at John. He clearly had no idea

who she was. She recalled the letter from the stuck up cow from 'up the Hill' in Inverness. "Why," she mused, "is John Urquhart confusing me with her. Surely we do not look alike?"

John looked at Alison. She looked different. The same... but different! And what was she doing here?

John's thoughts about Alison evaporated as, over Alison's shoulder, he could see Lesley, the stunning girl he had seen only briefly at the Nurses Home and the Caley. The girl he had written to for fifteen months, but had never actually spoken to. The girl who had broken his heart when she stopped writing.

"Excuse me, Alison," John said, to a startled Marie with the several aliases. It was the first time in her life that Marie had a man turn away from her.

John walked across the room. Smiley Jefferson was in deep conversation with Lesley. They broke off conversation as John approached.

Smiley was delighted to see John. He had followed John's Air Force progress quite keenly.

"I was just saying to Susan how nice it is to see so many people here," Smiley said.

John looked at Smiley, and looked at the girl. Recognition dawned upon him. It had been nearly fifteen years since he had danced with Susan Simpson, in the very room in which they were now standing. She looked radiant. It was hardly surprising that John had not recognised Susan. The girl, who used to wipe her nose on her sleeve, and run through the boys' toilets, had turned into a beautiful woman.

"Hello John," Susan said. "I've been hoping to speak to you for years. I saw you briefly at a dance in the Nurses Home, and again at the Caley, but on both occasions you rushed away."

Smiley knew when he was no longer required. Seeing

all the signs of a relationship blossoming, he left the couple to it.

John took Susan's hand.

"But," the thought suddenly struck him, "if this is Susan, who the hell is Lesley?"

The thought was still in John's mind when the blow was aimed at his head. It came from the man he had seen earlier with Irene Norman, the chap wearing the Gordon Highlanders tie. He knew he had seen him before, but had assumed that he was an old school pal.

John did two things at once. He remembered the squaddie from the Meeting Rooms and Malta, and he ducked. Just as a hand descended on his shoulder and the words, "I want you to accompany me to the station," were uttered in his ear.

Probationary Police Constable David Thomson got the full blow from the fist of the Gordon Highlander

The word "Run" rang out from John, as he grabbed Susan's hand and sped towards the door. Instinctively all the former pupils scattered. They had been taught from birth. On the command 'Run', you ran. You had no idea if you were the hunter, or the hunted. But you ran.

In the midst of all this P.P.C. David Thomson picked himself up off the floor. He could not believe what had just happened. He had just put his hand on Urquhart's shoulder when, out of the corner of his eye, he had seen Marie Winngate whom he had left only ten minutes before sitting in a locked police cell.

Chapter Sixty-Four

As John rushed out of the door to the assembly hall, still holding Susan's hand, he repeated his Playhouse Cinema trick. He ran straight into the door. In fairness this was not his fault. On hearing the fracas from inside the room, Chief Inspector Berk, who had been waiting outside with the riot squad, opened the door at the same time as John attempted to exit. The blow from the door knocked John out cold.

The riot squad rushed into the room, and were confronted by Violet MacDonald holding a cigarette lighter. The stage curtains in the assembly hall were on fire. Miss Goodall was sitting in a corner, holding her gold crucifix in front of her, muttering, "Not again, not again."

Jessie Williams and Betty Fraser had decided that this was a perfect moment to get their own back on Tommy Ross for his trick in the three-legged race, and were beating him over the head with, ironically enough, a chair leg. The leg had broken from the chair when they had smashed it over Tommy's head.

The police dogs ran into the room, and were confronted by Irene Norman and Tommy Brown. The police dogs took one look at Irene and Tommy and turned tail.

In the meantime Smiley Jefferson, Miss Shaw and Miss Fraser stood in the centre of the room. They had all reached the conclusion that the reunion had not been the brightest of ideas.

"We never have any trouble at this school," Smiley remarked, "until Urquhart and Roberts get together." He recalled the School Sports Day some fifteen years earlier. From the day that John and Sandy had left for High School, the school had operated perfectly normally. It was, in fact, the envy of most of the other schools.

Sirens were heard as black-marias, fire-engines and ambulances arrived. Twenty former pupils were taken to the police station. Six policemen, and one pupil, John, were taken to the Royal Northern Infirmary for treatment.

John had been at the Infirmary only half an hour when the decision was taken that he ought to be checked out thoroughly. He appeared to be suffering from concussion.

John was drifting in and out of consciousness, when he noticed the name badge of the fair-haired, blue-eyed nurse attending him.

'Nurse L Graham' the name badge stated.

Their eyes met.

John drifted back to sleep.

The following reports appeared in The Herald two days after the 'Kessie' reunion.

INVERNESS PRIMARY SCHOOL DESTROYED BY FIRE

On the evening of Friday 23 April, Kessock Primary School was completely destroyed as the result of a fire which began in the school assembly hall. A reunion party was being held at the time.

The presence of Chief Inspector Berk, thirty officers of the Highland Constabulary, and two fire engines, prevented any loss of life. The police and fire services were on a routine patrol of the Ferry district at the time.

A spokesman for the Highland Education Authority advises The Herald that there is no intention of re-building the school. Pupils will be dispersed to other primary schools in the town. The Herald further understands that a petition, from residents of the Hill District, demands that no pupils be transferred to schools in their area.

POLICE HOLD FRAUD SUSPECTS

Two suspects are being held in Inverness Police Station in connection with major fraud activities. A reliable source advises The Herald that a third person, a male, known as 'The Godfather', is helping the police with their enquiries.

Chapter Sixty-Five

John reported to the Police Station three days later. He had been discharged from hospital suffering no side effects. He was due to travel back to R.A.F. Northolt that day, but had been advised that the police wished to interview him 'in connection with their enquiries'.

Chief Inspector Berk interviewed John. He was desperate to get John for something. He suspected that John had not only bitten the police dog at the school sports some fifteen years before, but had also stolen the other dog. The Chief Inspector wanted this crime off his books. He also wanted to speak to John about his involvement with Marie Winngate.

John and the Chief Inspector were in the middle of the interview, when the Chief Constable intervened. They had a violent criminal and a master fraudster in the station who appeared to be accomplices. The Chief Constable wanted all the parties brought together.

Four hours after entering the station John sat in an interview room. Alison entered the room, very distraught.

"Do you know this woman?" the Chief Inspector asked.

John nodded. "Yes. Her name is Alison Forbes."

A moment later Marie Winngate was brought into the room.

"Do you know this woman?" the Chief Inspector asked.

John looked at both women. He had no idea which

one was Alison. He had no idea what was going on. Apart from their hairstyles the girls were identical.

It was P.P.C. Thomson who spotted the connection, and in doing so achieved his ambition of being a full constable. On checking the 'Prisoners in Custody Records' he noticed that Alison and Marie had the same birthday.

"I think it's time we brought in Mr Winngate" the Chief Constable said to the Chief Inspector.

One hour later Jocky Winngate walked into the room. It was as he suspected. The chickens had landed.

"Do you know either of these two women?" the Chief Constable asked Jocky.

Jocky looked at both Alison and Marie.

"Yes," he replied. "They are my twin daughters."

Alison looked at Jocky. At five feet two inches, and nine stone, he was hardly the image she had of her dead father. Apart from anything else he had been dead twenty-four years. Even worse, he was clearly from the Ferry.

Alison fainted.

Marie looked at Jocky and then looked at the Chief Constable.

"I wish to make a statement," she stated. "But only to the Chief Constable."

The Chief Constable nodded, seeing the possibility of locking up two serious criminals.

Marie and the Chief Constable were left in the room on their own.

Five minutes later the Chief Constable came out of the room and advised Chief Inspector Berk that, in the interest of national security, all charges would be dropped, and all concerned could leave the station.

The Chief Constable had no idea that the Lucy Chalmers he had been writing to for the previous two years, exchanging tales of lust and depravity, was in fact

Marie Winngate.

Despite having only seen a photograph of the Chief Constable, wearing make-up, a suspender belt, and a policewoman's uniform, Marie had recognised the Chief Constable straight away.

John arrived back at Northolt a day late from leave. He could not have cared less. He had a photograph of Susan in his pocket, on which she had written, 'All my love always'.

Chapter Sixty-Six

**INVERNESS
APRIL 2003**

The old man settled comfortably into his seat as the train left Inverness on the long journey to London.

It had been an interesting and nostalgic trip. So much had changed in his forty years absence from the town.

The previous afternoon he had visited the Ness Islands and had scattered John's ashes. Like his father and brother James, John had died of a heart attack. The Ness Islands had been silent. The sound of dance music had long since faded, but he swore he heard the sound of a solitary piper, playing a lament for the memories.

He visited the public house which John's father and elder brother had used. The clientele had changed. John never did have the chance to have a drink with his father, The taped music in the bar was playing traditional Scottish folk songs. The old man listened to the words of 'Grannies Heilan Hame' and 'Maggie' with tears in his eyes. He had a few drinks for John, and joined the Johnny Walker Choir as the whole pub sang 'Flower of Scotland' before being ejected from the pub. Some things had not changed.

The night before his return to England, he visited a ceilidh at a local hotel. He received a typical Highland welcome, sufficient to make him wonder what he had missed in the previous forty years. The social had been organised on behalf of the local old folks' residential home.

A tall striking figure of a man stood out in the party of residents from the home. The old man spoke to him during the course of the evening. The home resident introduced himself as, "Billy Wilson, from the Ferry."

As the train approached Kings Cross station, nearing the end of its journey, the train steward approached the old man. The train had changed dining car crews three times during the eight hour trip to London. Each steward, on hand-over, had passed the comment that the old man had seemed very subdued, as though his mind was elsewhere.

"Was your meal all right sir?" the steward asked, as he handed him the bill for his meal.

"Excellent," replied the old man, putting forward a credit card in payment.

The steward handed the old man the credit slip for signature.

The steward checked the signature against the card... Dr Leslie Graham.

Chapter Sixty-Seven

Kent. April 2003

On his return to Kent, Leslie and his wife Alison visited John's home.

John's wife, Susan, met them at the front door. John and Susan had been married nearly forty years. Susan had asked Leslie to go to Inverness to scatter John's ashes as she could not face a final parting from her childhood sweetheart. Who would have thought that John's first girlfriend, the girl with the runny nose at the 'Kessie School', would have ended up as his wife?

John and Susan kept in touch when John returned to the R.A.F. and Susan returned to Edinburgh University to continue her law studies following the 1962 'Kessie School Reunion'.

During John's first three years in the Royal Air Force, Susan had been at university. She had returned to Inverness only six times in the three year period, on each occasion to visit her sick aunt and her cousin, Leslie Graham, who was a nurse at the Royal Northern Infirmary.

Susan had known nothing about the trick that John's brother and Leslie had played on John. Susan had been with Leslie at the dance at the nurses home as his guest. She had recognised John as he was leaving the dance. Leslie had also been her companion when she had seen John at the Caley Ballroom.

Leslie had gone back to the Isle of Skye shortly after John had returned to El Adem in 1960. Leslie's mother had died, and he decided that he could no longer carry on the pretence with John. Leslie had realised that Susan was carrying a torch for John – indeed she had been since she was four years old. All she ever asked on her visits to Inverness was. "Has anybody heard from John Urquhart?" Leslie could hardly tell Susan that he was getting 'love letters' from John every week.

Sandy had been in the dark as well. James had given Sandy a verbal message that John should write to Nurse Lesley Graham. Sandy had assumed that the nurse was female. Sandy and John had never known the name of Susan's cousin, the small child she used to drag around the Ferry when he visited on holiday.

The truth came out at John and Susan's wedding in 1966. John was taken aback when Susan introduced the male nurse he had seen just before he passed out in the hospital following the Kessie school riot in 1962 as her cousin Leslie Graham. He was even more surprised when he realised that Leslie was accompanied to the wedding by Alison. It transpired that Leslie and Alison, both being nurses, had met at the Nurses Home Christmas dance in 1964. They had been courting since that time, and had eventually married in 1967. Leslie had met Alison's criteria of being a suitable catch by not being from the Ferry or Dalneigh. The Isle of Skye was a perfectly acceptable birthplace for a prospective husband. Leslie's acceptance at Medical School as a trainee doctor was the clincher. He was socially acceptable in Alison's eyes.

Leslie held in his hands the urn that Susan had given him to take to Inverness.

"Mission accomplished?" Susan asked.

Leslie nodded his head.

They wandered through the house into the back garden. Sandy was sitting in John's favourite garden seat.

The seat was close to the lilac bush that John had planted in memory of his parents. Sandy was recovering from major heart surgery, and had been advised to rest for several months. Sandy's wife, Jean, was also in the garden, the same Jean who had shouted 'they're having sex' when she had run out of the Anderson shelter sixty years before.

"How are the memoirs coming on?" Leslie asked Sandy.

"Fine," replied Sandy, "I'm just at the part in 1990 when I took the Chief Executive of the company I worked for to a posh restaurant in London, it was arranged by John. When we got there we discovered that it was a pole dancing club. It probably would have been all right, but then my boss realised that his wife was one of the pole dancers."

Susan turned to Jean. "All the arrangements in place?" she asked.

"Yes," Jean replied. "All the replies have been received. Over forty acceptances, including one from Lady Castello. We remember her better as Marie Winngate."

"That's not bad," Susan stated. "Considering we're all in our sixties or seventies, getting forty of us to a school reunion party is quite an achievement. It's a great pity that 'The Kessie' was burnt to the ground after the 1962 reunion, and that we have to hold the reunion elsewhere"

"At the Caley hotel?" Alison asked.

"Yes," Leslie replied, "although it's no longer called the Caley."

"Roll on next month," said Sandy, "It will be good to see all the old faces."